Stickleback

ENGLAND'S GLORY

STICKLEBACK CRE[...]N & D'ISRAELI

ENGLAND'S GLORY

IAN EDGINTON
Writer

D'ISRAELI
Artist

Creative Director and CEO: Jason Kingsley
Chief Technical Officer: Chris Kingsley
2000 AD Editor in Chief: Matt Smith
Graphic Design: Simon Parr & Luke Preece
Marketing and PR: Keith Richardson
Repro Assistant: Kathryn Symes

Graphic Novels Editor: Jonathan Oliver
Designer: Simon Parr
Original Commissioning Editor: Matt Smith

Originally serialised in *2000 AD* Progs 2007, 1518-1525, 2008, 1567-1577.

Published by Rebellion, Riverside House, Osney Mead, Oxford OX2 0ES, UK.
www.rebellion.co.uk

ISBN: 978-1-905437-74-0
Printed in Malta by Gutenberg Press
Manufactured in the EU by LPPS Ltd., Wellingborough, NN8 3PJ, UK.
First printing: August 2008
10 9 8 7 6 5 4 3 2 1

Printed on FSC Accredited Paper

A CIP catalogue record for this book is available from the British Library.

For information on other *2000 AD* graphic novels, or if you have any comments on this book, please email books@2000ADonline.com

To find out more about *2000 AD*, visit www.2000ADonline.com

"No, Mister Bond. I expect you to die!'

WHY IT'S GOOD TO BE BAD

It's long been acknowledged that bad guys possess a certain desirability to which we all aspire, even though we probably wouldn't admit it out loud. How often have we heard that despite their better judgement, all the ladies love a bad boy. Take Dracula for instance, a blood lusting, revenant, Wallachian warlord he may be, but he knows how to turn a girls head.

Basically bad guys are cool. They have better clothes, their own island or hollow volcano, snappier dialogue and (usually until the last page or final reel) they get away with murder. Dracula. Fantomas. Moriarty. Diabolik. The black hats have a lot more fun. Even movie actors acknowledge that if you can't play the hero, be the bad guy.

When a new Bond movie is announced, after whoever's playing the next 'Bond girl' we want to know who the villain is? Bond is an interesting character in that he displays all the aspects of a villain yet he's on our side. A perfect example of this is in *Doctor No* where he calmly questions the traitorous Professor Dent who'd just emptied his gun into Bond's bed, thinking he was in it. When he's done, Bond simply kills him in cold blood with the line: 'You've had your six.'

The Punisher, Bond and even Batman all occupy this questionable, grey area. Batman is especially intriguing as he is all about control. As a child his parents were murdered in front of him. As a young adult, he vowed to use his wits and wealth to impose order on Gotham City. However, it's impossible, entropy and chaos are the natural, eventual order of things. To quote William Butler Yeats:

'Things fall apart; the centre cannot hold;
Mere anarchy is loosed upon the world.'

And who is the prince of anarchy but The Joker? It takes just a small step across that line to become the thing you hate. Evil is seductive, that's what makes it fun.

We like villains because they appeal to that tiny whisper of criminality that curls in our ear like smoke. Whether it's not admitting when we've been undercharged for something or wondering what would happen if you gave that person on the crowded underground platform in front of you a little nudge, just as the Tube was pulling in?

You don't? Well it must be me then, but I digress...

Having written my fair share of heroes over the years, I felt the desire to don the black hat for a while. British comics and pulps have a great tradition of placing the villain squarely at centre stage. These range from the Victorian and Edwardian Penny Dreadfuls depicting the dastardly doings of Varney the Vampire, Spring-Heeled Jack and the Blue Dwarf, to the pages of *Thunder, Lion* and *Valiant* comics in the 1960's and 70's, home to The Spider, the Black Max and the early adventures of The Steel Claw who started out as a thief and all round bad egg.

To this end, I and my partner in crime, artiste extraordinary D'Israeli – the ballroom dancing Esperantologist – created Stickleback, The Pope of Crime. He secretly presides over the criminal fraternity of a fantastical, grotesque, Gormenghast-style old London town. Surrounded by his coterie of freakish compatriots. we watch as he weaves his web of vice and intrigue around the city snaring innocent and guilty alike. However, where Stickleback is concerned nothing is quite so straightforward. The man himself is a grave mystery. A nefarious enigma about whom there are too few answer... or too many. Which of course is why you are here.

You hold in your hand a diversion, a confection and entertainment. It is also a paper puzzle box in which, if you look carefully, you may possibly uncover the answers to the conundrum that is Stickleback... if that really is his name.

See you on the underground. Mind the gap.

Ian Edginton
June 2008

MOTHER LONDON

Script: Ian Edginton
Art: D'Israeli
Letters: Ellie De Ville

Originally published in *2000 AD* Progs 2007, 1518-1525

ALBION.
BASTARDS!
CONNIVING PRIESTS! LET US LOOSE OR I'LL TEAR YOUR SHITTING THROATS OUT WITH MY TEETH!
THAT'S HARDLY AN INCENTIVE, NOW IS IT?
SLY, BACKSTABBING SONS OF WHORES! THIS IS HOW YOU REPAY OUR BLOOD AND SERVICE?
YOUR HEARTH AND HOMES ENDURE BECAUSE OF US. MY BROTHER AND I HAVE PUT MORE FLITCHES IN THE DIRT FOR YOU THAN A MAN MAY SIRE IN A LIFETIME.
YOUR DAUGHTERS HAVE THEIR LIVES AND THEIR MAIDENHEADS, YOUR WIVES ARE NOT WIDOWS, FOR WE STOOD FAST IN OUR DUTY, KEEPING THE CELT AND NORTH-MEN FROM YOUR DOOR. NOW WE ARE REPAID WITH THIS... TREACHERY?

DON'T BLAME THEM. THIS WAS **MY** CHOICE. THEY DON'T COME TO GAWP BUT TO HONOUR YOU.
WHAT I DO THIS DAY, THE SACRIFICE I CALL UPON YOU TO MAKE, WILL BENEFIT MORE THAN JUST THOSE GATHERED HERE BUT **GENERATIONS** TO COME. WE NEED YOU TO BE GUARDIANS STILL.

I WAS THERE AT YOUR BIRTH, WHEN YOUR MOTHER BLED HER LIFE INTO THE EARTH SO THAT YOU MIGHT LIVE.
YOU WERE A GIFT FROM THE GODS. YOU HAVE BEEN OUR CONSTANTS, OUR PILLARS, OUR SUN AND MOON—

—**GOG** AND **MAGOG**.
BUT YOU ARE LONG IN THE SHANK AND TOOTH NOW. TIME NAGS AT YOUR BONES, GREY CREEPS UPON YOUR TEMPLES. EVERYTHING HAS ITS SEASON AND YOUR AUTUMN DAYS ARE UPON YOU.

WE'LL OUTLIVE YOU, YOU POX-PIZZLED OLD GOAT!
LET HIM FINISH.

DO YOU WISH THE REMORSELESS DECLINE INTO WINTER, KNOWING YOUR BEST YEARS ARE BEHIND YOU? TO SEE THOSE YOU FOUGHT TO DEFEND INEVITABLY FALL TO THE INVADERS' SWORDS WHILE YOU ARE TOO WEAK TO WIELD YOUR OWN?

WHAT WOULD YOU HAVE US DO?
BROTHER?

SURRENDER YOURSELF AND LIVE FOREVER. YOUR BONES SHALL BE THE ROOTS OF THE WORLD, YOUR FLESH THE MEAT OF THE EARTH. YOUR SOULS SHALL INHABIT THIS DWELLING PLACE AND THROUGH IT YOU SHALL GUIDE THE LIFE OF AGES.
SO BE IT.
BROTHER, THINK HARD. IS THIS YOUR WILL?
IT IS. HE SPEAKS A BITTER TRUTH BUT TRUTH NEVERTHELESS.
THEN WHERE YOU LEAD, I SHALL FOLLOW.
BE ABOUT YOUR WORK, OLD MAN. WE WOULD BE IN OUR NEW BEDS COME NIGHTFALL.

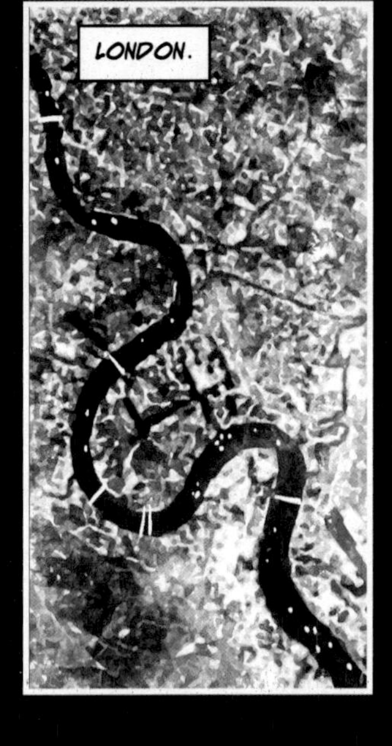
LONDON.

WELCOME TO MY WORLD...
ZOPTO-BENSOL

DO NOT BE AFRAID, MY FRIENDS. DEATH IS NOT THE END BUT MERELY A TRANSITION FROM ONE REALM TO ANOTHER.

THE DEARLY DEPARTED TREAD A PATH NOT OPEN TO US. HOWEVER, IF WE ARE FORTUNATE AND CIRCUMSTANCES AUSPICIOUS, WE MAY PEER BEYOND THE GREY VEIL FOR A BRIEF EXCHANGE.
BARRETT'S STOUT
INVALIDS

Abdul Alhazred
Spiritualist
AFTER ALL, THAT IS WHY YOU ARE HERE, IS IT NOT?
SHALL WE BEGIN? GALATEA, THE LIGHTS, PLEASE. ALL BUT THIS ONE.

DO... DO WE HAVE TO, UM, HOLD HANDS?

HA HA HA! NO, MY BOY, ONLY IF YOU WISH IT. NOR DO YOU HAVE TO CLOSE YOUR EYES. I AM NO CHARLATAN TABLE-RAPPER, DRUM BETWEEN MY KNEES AND BEDSHEETS ON STRINGS!
THE LAMP HERE STAYS LIT, YOUR EYES WIDE OPEN. ALTHOUGH, IF SOMETHING OTHERWORLDLY SHOULD MANIFEST, I'D ADVISE NOT TOUCHING IT. SUCH THINGS CAN BE... DISTURBING.
NOW, WE MUST ALL CONCENTRATE ON THE SAME SPOT. OUR MINDS SHALL OPEN THE GATEWAY TO THE BEYOND. CLEAR YOUR THOUGHTS AND FOCUS UPON THE LIGHT...

FREE YOURSELVES OF ALL YOUR WORRIES AND WOES! DIVEST YOURSELVES OF LIFE'S ENCUMBRANCES AND **SURRENDER** TO THE LIGHT!

SURRENDER YOURSELVES TO ITS RADIANCE... SURRENDER YOURSELVES... TO **ME**!

SURRENDER!
LEN? YOU ALL RIGHT?

ARE WE SET? GOOD. I THINK WE SHALL COMMENCE WITH YOU AND YOUR ENIGMATIC LADY WIFE, CAPTAIN D'ASCOYNE.
WHERE DO YOU KEEP YOUR SAFE, YOUR STRONGBOX? IS IT KEY OR COMBINATION?
NO BOX... TEN BOBS' WORTH OF THRUPPENCES AND MY OLD DAD'S WATCH... IN A SOCK UNDER THE MATTRESS...
WHAT? WHAT NONSENSE IS THIS?
LEN! LADS! ON YOUR FEET! THE JIG'S UP!
POLICE OFFICERS! NOBODY MOVE!
BLAST!
HA HA HA! YOU MAKE A FINE FIGURE OF A FEMALE, MY FRIEND, BUT YOU LOOK BETTER WITH THE VEIL ON!
OF COURSE.
SKTTASHH!
NO!

WHUSSIS? WHAS GOIN' ON?
WE'VE BEEN RUMBLED! SNAP OUT OF IT!

GALATEA! **KILL THEM ALL!**

NOW THEN, MISS, I'LL ASK YOU TO—
WAHH!
PLAYIN' DRESS UP AS WELL, ARE YOU, CHUMMY?

WELL, I AIN'T ADVERSE TO PUNCHIN' EITHER A LAD OR LADY IN THE SNOOT!
KHUNGG!

GAH!

GOD LOVE US AND SAVE US!

GUK...

BDAM!
BDAM!

MUCH OBLIGED, SIR!

STOP THAT TURK!

YAAH!

SKRTTTKKKK!

THUNK
SHUNKK!
OH MY GIDDY AUNT!
DON'T LOOK AT ME!
DON'T LOOK AT ME!

COVE'S NAME WAS **PHILO THYNNE**, PROFESSOR OF MECHANICAL ENGINEERING AT LONDON UNIVERSITY, 'TIL HE UPPED AND RESIGNED THREE YEARS AGO.

HE SACKED ALL HIS STAFF TOO BUT WHEN THE BAKER AN' BUTCHER'S BOY CALLED, THEY SAID THERE WAS A NEW LOT. A STIFF AN' SURLY BUNCH.

Detective Valentine Bey
Sergeant Leonard Chipps
PROBABLY MORE OF HIS CLOCKWORK CHUMS.

HE USED THAT MECHANICAL TURK AS A SPIRITUALIST FRONT, MESMERISING HIS VICTIMS INTO FEEDING HIM DETAILS ON HOW TO CRACK THEIR HOUSES.
WHICH'S HOW WE GOT ON TO HIM.

HE USED THE MONEY TO BUILD MORE OF HIS MACHINES BUT ALSO TO SUSTAIN HIMSELF IN THAT GROTESQUE **GREENHOUSE** OF HIS. IT WAS HARDLY THE DEN OF A CRIMINAL GENIUS RELISHING HIS SPOILS. IT WAS MORE LIKE A **REFUGE**.
HE WAS AFRAID OF SOMETHING?

OR SOMEONE...

THIS COULD BE THE CLUE WE'VE BEEN LOOKING FOR, LEN. WE'VE FINALLY GOT A LEAD ON—
We've finally got a lead on
STICKLEBACK

SUSSEX DOWNS.

WE GOT A GOOD 'EAD O'STEAM A-BREWIN' NOW, SERGEANT POTTS! WE'LL DO YOU PROUD, SO WE WILL, 'AVE YOU IN AHEAD O'TIME!
BETTER MORE HASTE, LESS SPEED, MISTER HARBOTTLE. ESPECIALLY GIVEN OUR **CARGO**.

'ERE! THERE'S SOMETHIN' ON THE LINE...

'IT'S A **COW**!'

WE CAN'T STOP! WE'VE GOT ORDERS!
GIVE IT A TOOT, ALBERT, THAT'LL PUT TH' WIND UP TH'BUGGER!

IT'S NOT SHIFTIN'!
IT BLOODY BETTER...

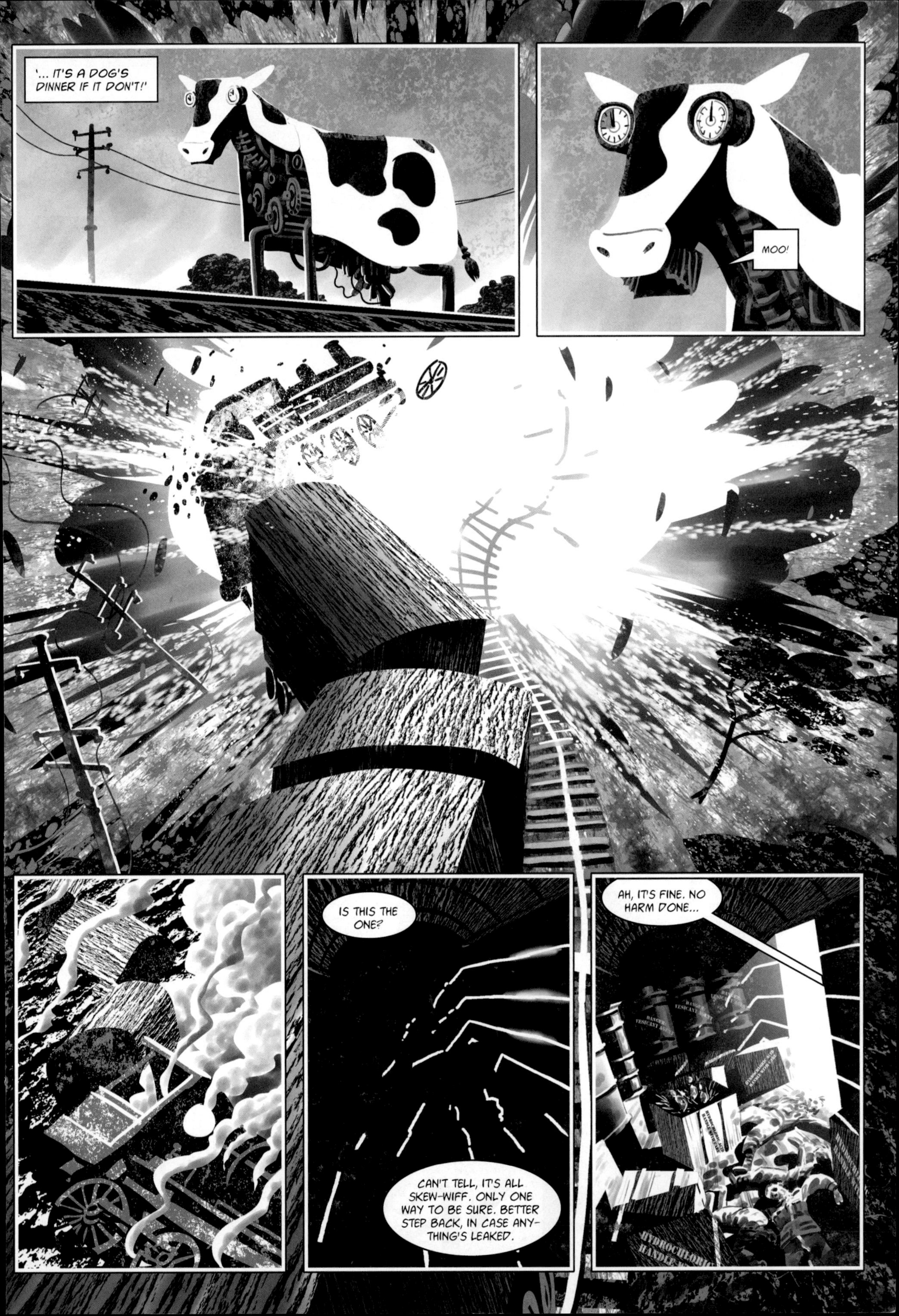
'... IT'S A DOG'S DINNER IF IT DON'T!'
MOO!
IS THIS THE ONE?
CAN'T TELL, IT'S ALL SKEW-WIFF. ONLY ONE WAY TO BE SURE. BETTER STEP BACK, IN CASE ANYTHING'S LEAKED.
AH, IT'S FINE. NO HARM DONE...

TELL ME, DETECTIVE BEY, WHAT ASPECT OF THE WORD 'NO' DO YOU FAIL TO COMPREHEND?
CHIEF CONSTABLE LIME, SIR, I BELIEVE PROFESSOR THYNNE HAS HAD DEALINGS WITH STICKLEBACK. DEALINGS WHICH TURNED SOUR, HENCE HIM HIDING IN THAT GHASTLY GLASSHOUSE TO AVOID THE EXOTIC EXECUTIONS WE KNOW STICKLEBACK MEETS OUT.

STICKLEBACK! STICKLEBACK! IT IS A NAME CONJURED FROM A CHILD'S NURSERY RHYME! BESIDES RUMOUR, SPECULATION AND HALF-TRUTH, DO YOU HAVE EVEN A JOT OF EVIDENCE THIS CHARACTER EXISTS?
IF THIS INFANTILE ENIGMA IS QUITE THE POPE OF CRIME YOU IMAGINE, WHY IS THERE NOT ONE WORD OF HIM ON THE STREET? IN THE GIN-SWILLS AND ALE HOUSES?
FEAR, SIR. THOSE WHO CROSS HIM MEET THEIR END IN TERRIBLE WAYS, ENSURING TIGHT LIPS ALL ROUND.
THYNNE'S CON GAME WASN'T DONE OUT OF AVARICE BUT TERROR. HE USED HIS AUTOMATA TO ACCRUE FUNDS TO MAINTAIN HIS SORRY STATE. HE IS OUR ONLY LIVE WITNESS TO THE FIEND'S EXISTENCE. IF I COULD QUESTION HIM FURTHER—

IMPOSSIBLE. PROFESSOR THYNNE IS MENTALLY DISTURBED. I HAVE HAD HIM COMMITTED. THAT IS MY FINAL WORD.
BUT WE SPENT MONTHS BUILDING THIS CASE—

THEN YOU WILL HAVE TO HITCH YOUR CAREER ASPIRATIONS TO ANOTHER STAR. THIS ONE HAS FALLEN.
BE CAREFUL YOURS DOES NOT FOLLOW. GOOD DAY.

THE JOLLY CRIPPLE
THAT SLY, SNIDE, MISERABLE OLD BUGGER!

HE PULLED THE BLOODY RUG OUT FROM UNDER US AN' WE STOOD THERE LIKE A PAIR O'LEMONS AN' TOOK IT! AFTER ALL THE SWEAT WE PUT IN!
S'NOT LIKE WE HAD A **CHOICE** THOUGH, WAS IT, BOSS?

OH, NOW HE FINDS HIS VOICE! COULDN'T PIPE UP WHEN IT COUNTED, COULD YOU?
I DIDN'T... I THOUGHT... WELL, HE **IS** THE CHIEF!

YES, QUITE RIGHT. I'M SORRY, LEN, I'M JUS' SOUNDING OFF. IF YOU'D STUCK YOUR NECK OUT, YOU'D HAVE ONLY HAD IT BITTEN OFF TOO.
WORD T'THE WISE: Y'WANT A FUTURE IN THE FORCE, STANDIN' NEXT T'**ME** ISN'T THE BEST PLACE T'BE.

SEE THIS? IT DOESN'T RUB OFF, HENCE THE 'DARK DETECTIVE' NOM DE PLUME. DON'T TELL ME YOU'VE NOT HEARD IT. I'VE HEARD 'EM ALL...
... 'SPECIALLY THE BIT 'BOUT HOW MY FATHER BROUGHT HIMSELF BACK A LITTLE BIT OF **EASTERN PROMISE** WHILE SERVING QUEEN AND COUNTRY IN THE COLONIES.

YOU KNOW, MY MOTHER ALWAYS SAID SHE WAS THE GRANDDAUGHTER OF THE ALI PASHA HIMSELF.
GRANDMAMMA ESCAPED THE MASSACRE OF HER FAMILY AND WAS RESCUED BY A MYSTERIOUS FRENCH COUNT, WHO USED HIS FORTUNE TO VISIT JUST RETRIBUTION UPON THEIR MURDERERS....

I THINK THAT'S WHY SHE WAS SO PROUD WHEN I JOINED THE FORCE. BOTH SHE AND MY FATHER FELT STRONGLY ABOUT DOING THE RIGHT THING.
IT'S A BLESSING THEY NEVER LIVED TO SEE THIS.

SPEAKIN' OF WHICH, IT'S HIGH TIME YOU HEADED OFF HOME TO YOUR FINE MISSUS!
AH, THAS' TRUE! BLESS YOU, LEN!
YOU'RE A GENT AND A SCHOLAR!
'COURSE I AM.
CAB!
EXCUSE ME, SIR, DO I HAVE THE PLEASURE OF ADDRESSING DETECTIVE VALENTINE BEY?
I AM HE!
SPLENDID!
GOOD SHOT, SIR!
FUGO FABOI!
NO, I WASN'T BEING SARCASTIC!
FUGU!
OH, THERE'S JUST NO PLEASING SOME PEOPLE...

RUN, RUN, RUN,
JUST AS FAST AS
YOU CAN!

RUN
AND HIDE FROM
THE STICKLEBACK
MAN!

HE COMES
WITH A HOOK AND
HE COMES WITH
A SHIV!

'DON'T LOOK BACK
OR HE'LL DO YOU IN!'
UHHH...

ONE LUMP OR
TWO?
WHUSSA—?

PUNCH & JUDY
I SAID,
ONE LUMP OR
TWO?

DR. LAO
BEST MAKE IT TWO. GOOD FOR SHOCK.
LITTLE TONGA'S **KNOCKOUT JUICE** CAN MESS WITH YOUR NOGGIN SOMETHING VILE, 'SPECIALLY ON TOP OF ALL THAT ALE Y'NECKED LAST NIGHT.
YOU!
SAY MY NAME, Y'MAKE ME REAL!
STICKLEBACK!
PLEASE, SIR, REMAIN SEATED.
UFF!
TSK, LOOK AT THAT! DARJEELING NEVER SHIFTS OUTTA SILK!
THAT WAS UNCOUTH AN' UNCALLED FOR. WHAT'D I DO TO YOU, EH?
YOU'RE **VERMIN**! MUCH OF THE CITY'S MISERY IS DUE TO YOU!
OH, YOU THINK? LET ME TELL YOU, MISTER POLICEMAN, I GIVES THE PEOPLE PRECISELY WHAT THEY **WANT**...
... ME DOXIES ARE CLEAN, ME GIN AIN'T WATERED, AND ME OPIUM AIN'T CUT WITH RAT SHIT AN' SAWDUST LIKE SOME I COULD MENTION. I PROVIDES A FAIR SERVICE AT A FAIR PRICE.

YOU WERE BORN SCUM AND YOU'LL DIE SCUM!
MURDER ME AND HAVE DONE WITH IT! THAT'S WHY I'M HERE, ISN'T IT?
I DON'T WISH YOU ILL, FAR FROM IT. THE WORLD'S A COLD, CRUEL PLACE, VALENTINE. WE DO WHAT WE MUST TO SURVIVE.
LOOK AT YOU — A FINE FIGURE OF A MAN. TALL, HANDSOME, DASHING, ALL YOUR OWN TEETH. YET THE BITTERNESS ROILS OFF YOU IN WAVES. WHY?
NOW ME, I GUTTED MY MOTHER LIKE A FISH THE DAY I WAS BORN. I CAME INTO THE WORLD A MURDERER.
ALL OF US HERE HAVE LABOURED UNDER SOME FORM OF ILL-OMENED STAR. SHUNNED, MOCKED, ABUSED BY THE WORLD, WE MAKE OUR WAY IN IT THE ONLY WAY WE CAN AND MAINTAIN SOME DIGNITY...
... AS VILLAINS? INCIDENTALLY, YOUR ACCENT'S SLIPPING. WHAT WAS THAT, ROTHERHITHE BY WAY OF ETON AND HARROW?
YOU'RE A CLEVER MAN, VALENTINE. YES, WE PLAY THE VILLAIN BUT WE DON'T PISS ON OUR DOORSTEP. IF FOLK ARE FOOL ENOUGH TO WANT MY DRINK, DRUGS AND DOLLIES, WHO AM I TO ARGUE?
I ALSO DO WHAT YOU BOBBIES CANNOT — I KEEP THE STREETS LAWFUL. I MAKE SURE EACH KIDDIE SLEEPS WITH A FULL BELLY. A MAN BEATS HIS WIFE, I SEE HE DOESN'T DO IT TWICE.
AND IN RETURN IT BUYS THEIR SILENCE. I SHOULD'VE KNOWN, THE CARROT WORKS BETTER THAN THE STICK!
EXCEPT.... SOMETHING'S HAPPENED. UPSET THE APPLECART. YOU'RE NOT SUCH HAPPY FAMILIES ANYMORE. THAT'S WHY THYNNE TRIED TO DO A RUNNER ON YOU.

THYNNE! FOREVER STICKING HIS DICK IN HIS TIN-PLATE TARTS! HE WAS A LIABILITY, A TURNCOAT FOR THEM!
WHO?
THE CITY FATHERS! NOT A GANG OR A MOB, MORE LIKE A BROTHERHOOD, AN ORDER, LIKE MONKS OR MASONS. THEY'VE BEEN WAITING IN THE WINGS LONG AS I CAN RECALL BUT LAST YEAR, OUT OF THE BLUE, THEY MADE THEIR MOVE...
... TOOK OUT A DOZEN FIRMS AND FAMILIES IN A HEARTBEAT. THE PECKHAM BOYS, THE WALFORD QUEENS, GONE IN A NIGHT! THEY WEREN'T CONTENT WITH A SLICE — BASTARDS WANTED THE WHOLE PIE!
FORGIVE ME IF I DON'T SHED A TEAR.
OH, YOU WILL. SEE, THESE AREN'T STREET OR SHIFTY — THEY'RE CONNECTED. THEY'RE SOV'D AND WELL HEELED, HIGH UP AS YOU LIKE!
THIS ISN'T ABOUT RUNNIN' THE UNDERWORLD BUT THE WHOLE SHOW! THEY WANT THE CITY FOR THEMSELVES! TOP TO BOTTOM, INSIDE AND OUT! LAWFUL AND LAWLESS!
WHICH'S WHY I NEED YOUR HELP.
GO TO HELL!
I'VE BEEN WATCHIN' YOU, BOY. I LIKE YOU. YOU'RE LIKE US, AN OUTSIDER. THEY TREAT YOU LIKE SOMETHIN' THEY STEPPED IN, ALL 'CAUSE Y'GRAVY DON'T WIPE OFF.
YOU DON'T KNOW ME!
SAYS YOU. EVEN YOUR OLD DAD GOT SO DISGUSTED THAT THE COUNTRY HE FOUGHT FOR SHOULD TREAT HIS LOVELY WIFE WORSE THAN A DOG, HE DITCHED HIS FAMILY NAME AND TOOK HERS.
JUST MAKES YOU BURN, DOESN'T IT? THE INJUSTICE. IT'S WHY YOU BECAME A COPPER, TO PUT THE WORLD TO RIGHTS.

NOTHING YOU SAY WILL CONVINCE ME TO HELP YOU!
EVEN IF I WAS TO TELL YOU THE GREAT MAN HIMSELF, **CHIEF CONSTABLE DELIUS LIME**, WAS ONE OF THE CITY FATHERS?
ABSURD.
MISTER PEEPERS, MISTER LUG. A MOMENT.
'OW
DO.
THANK YOU, GENTLEMEN.
HERE — PAPERS, PICTURES, THE WORKS. CHAPTER AND VERSE. THEY AS GOOD AS CATCH HIM WITH HIS HAND IN THE TILL AND HIS JOHN THOMAS IN THE CHAMBERMAID.
ALL FAKED, NO DOUBT.
THAT'S FOR YOU TO DECIDE. TAKE THEM HOME, HAVE THEM EXAMINED, ALTHOUGH BE CAREFUL WHO YOU SHOW THEM TO.
YOU'RE LETTING ME GO? WHY?
TRUST, MY BOY. YOU'LL SOON LEARN, IT'S ALL A MATTER OF WHO YOU CAN TRUST...

LONDON, MOTHER LONDON... SHE'S A CONTRARY OLD COW.
ONE TEAT'S SWEET, THE OTHER'S SOUR, BUT SHE'S THE ONLY MUM WE'VE GOT AN' NO ONE'S TAKIN' HER FROM US.
LIGHT ME, FIERY JACK.
MMM... TA.
DO YOU THINK HE WAS CONVINCED, THAT JOHNNY-ON-THE-BEAT?
NOT AN OUNCE OR JOT, BUT THAT WAS NEVER THE GAME OF IT.
WHAT I'VE DONE IS STUCK A QUESTION MARK IN HIS BRAIN, PUT A LITTLE ITCH IN HIS MIND HE CAN'T HELP BUT SCRATCH.
I'VE BAITED AN' CAST M'LINE...
'... NOW WE SIT AN' WAIT TO SEE WHAT HE REELS IN.'
MARIAH!
FESTIVAL Rd.
MARIAH!

VAL!
OH THANK GOD YOU'RE SAFE! I DIDN'T KNOW IF HE'D DONE SOMETHING TO YOU ALL! PLAYED SOME SICK, TWISTED **TRICK** ON ME!

WHAT? WHO?
VAL, WHERE'VE YOU **BEEN**?

I'M SORRY I WAS GONE ALL NIGHT. IT WASN'T INTENDED, BELIEVE ME.
ALL NIGHT? YOU'VE BEEN MISSING FOR **TWO DAYS!**

TWO... DAYS?

BLOODY HELL! THE PRODIGAL RETURNS — 'SCUSE MY FRENCH!
LEN? WHAT'RE YOU DOING HERE?

Y'MISSUS HAS BEEN AT HER WITS' END, BOSS. NO ONE'S SEEN HIDE NOR HAIR OF YOU SINCE Y'LEFT THE JOLLY CRIPPLE.
WE'VE HAD THE CRUSHERS PULLIN' DOUBLE-SHIFTS ON THE SCOUR. I'VE BEEN SITTIN' THE WATCH HERE WITH MRS B AND THE KIDDIES, IN CASE YOU TURNED UP.

THE CHILDREN!
ARE SAFE AND ASLEEP, FINALLY!
WHERE'VE YOU BEEN, MY LOVE? WHAT'S HAPPENED? YOU LOOK A STATE!

I WAS DRUGGED, KIDNAPPED AND TAKEN FOR AN AUDIENCE WITH NO LESS THAN THE POPE OF CRIME HIMSELF — STICKLEBACK!
HE WANTS ME TO BE HIS NEW BEST CHUM. FED ME SOME FLANNEL ABOUT A SECRET ORDER — THE CITY FATHERS — INTENT ON TAKING CONTROL OF THE CAPITAL FROM THE SLUMS TO HIGH OFFICE AND ALL POINTS IN BETWEEN.

HE TRIED TO SWAY ME WITH THESE — DOCUMENTS INCRIMINATING LIME AS A RANKING MEMBER OF THIS COVERT FRATERNITY.
THEN WE'D BEST SHOW 'EM TO THE OLD MAN. PROVE WE WERE ON TH'RIGHT TRACK ALL ALONG.

WHAT'S IN 'EM ANYWAY?
I DON'T KNOW EXACTLY. I'VE NOT HAD CHANCE TO READ THEM.
QUESTION IS, STICKLEBACK WOULD KNOW WE'D SHOW THEM TO LIME FIRST, SO WHAT'S HIS GAME? HE'S WORKING TO A DESIGN I CAN'T FATHOM YET...

SO WHY NOT READ THEM NOW?
NO, I... I STILL THINK WE'RE BETTER OFF GIVIN' 'EM TO THE GUV'NOR. CARDS ON THE TABLE, LIKE.

NOT YET. HERE, HIDE THEM. TELL NO ONE. I'LL SEND FOR THEM SOON.

VAL... I'M AFRAID.
DON'T BE. I WOULD HARRY THE VERY HALLS OF HELL BEFORE I LET ANY HARM COME TO YOU. BE STRONG.
I HAVE TO SEE CHIEF CONSTABLE LIME STRAIGHT AWAY, BUT I'LL BE BACK SOON.

Y'BETTER BRACE Y'SELF. LAST TIME I SAW HIM, HIS FACE WAS AS PUFFED UP AN' PURPLE AS A BISHOP'S HELMET — 'SCUSE M'FRENCH!

WELL, WELL. THAT IS AN EXTRAORDINARY TALE. QUITE THE PENNY DREADFUL, I'M SURE.
I, UH... YOU BELIEVE ME?
DETECTIVE BEY, DESPITE OUR FREQUENT CROSSING SWORDS, DESPITE MY DISLIKE OF YOUR ARROGANCE AND ATTITUDE, I KNOW YOU TO BE A THOROUGH AND HONEST OFFICER OF THE LAW.
I AM NOT THE MANNER OF MAN WHO WISHES HIS MEN TO LIKE HIM. I AM A GENERAL, DESPATCHING MY FORCES AGAINST THE EVER-RISING TIDE OF THE UNSCRUPULOUS, UNWASHED AND UNGODLY.
ALL I DEMAND IS YOU OBEY MY WORD AS IF IT WERE HANDED DOWN FROM THE ALMIGHTY HIMSELF. NOW, AS YOU ARE NOT CUSTOMARILY GIVEN TO DELUSIONAL ALCOHOLIC BINGES OR OPIUM JAGS, I MUST ASSUME YOU ARE TELLING THE TRUTH.
THEN I MUST SEE PROFESSOR THYNNE. HE IS THE ONLY WINDOW WE HAVE INTO STICKLEBACK'S WORLD—
THAT'S NOT POSSIBLE. THYNNE DIED THIS MORNING, FROM A SUDDEN ATTACK OF DENGUE FEVER, I'M TOLD.
POISONED, MORE LIKE! STICKLEBACK HAS A NUMBER OF EXOTIC ASSASSINS AT HIS BECK AND CALL!
THEN WE ARE BACK TO SQUARE ONE.
WELL, PERHAPS NOT. THERE IS SOMETHING...
NOK! NOK!
NOT NOW!

ARE YOU DEAF?
I'M SORRY, SIR. IT'S JUST THAT...
WELL, THERE'S BEEN AN ACCIDENT, BOSS... DETECTIVE BEY.

WHAT DO YOU MEAN?
IT'S YOUR **HOUSE**, BOSS—

'... IT'S **GONE**!'

IT BEGINS... AT LAST!

MARIAH!
MASTER CRIMINAL STICKLEBACK HAS GIVEN SCOTLAND YARD DETECTIVE VALENTINE BEY DOCUMENTS CLAIMING TO PROVE THAT SECRET SOCIETY THE CITY FATHERS ARE PLANNING ON TAKING OVER THE CAPITAL'S UNDERWORLD. NOW, BEY'S HOME HAS BEEN BURNT TO THE GROUND...
MARIAH!
STEADY, GUV! EASY!
F'GOD'S SAKE, LET ME GO! I WON'T LEAVE THEM!
THERE'S NOTHIN' Y'CAN DO FOR 'EM! GO IN THERE, YOU'LL BE KILLED Y'SELF!
THEY'VE GONE. THEY'RE NOT SUFFERIN', THEY'RE IN THE ARMS OF THE LORD NOW.
BUT I CAN'T... I WON'T... THEIR BODIES ARE STILL IN THERE!
OH CHRIST, LEN... HOW DID THIS HAPPEN?
WE BOTH KNOW HOW.
STICKLEBACK?
THE DEVIL HIMSELF!

BUT, NO... IT DOESN'T MAKE SENSE! HE HAD ME IN HIS GRASP, COULD'VE DONE WHAT HE LIKED... BUT HE GAVE ME THE **DOCUMENTS** INSTEAD. WHY DO THAT, THEN THIS?
'CAUSE HE'S A VICIOUS SHITHOUSE, WHO WANTS T'MAKE YOU SQUIRM AN' SUFFER! IT'S HOW HE WORKS, MESSIN' WITH YOUR HEAD! LOOK WHAT HE DROVE THYNNE TO!

SEE WHAT HE'S DOIN' TO YOU! HE'S MURDERED YOUR FAMILY AN' YOU'RE LOOKIN' FOR WAYS NOT TO BLAME HIM! HE DIDN'T WANT YOU SHOWIN' THOSE PAPERS TO THE CHIEF, THAT'S REASON ENOUGH, AIN'T IT?

EXCEPT HE KNEW FULL WELL I **WOULD**. HE'D PROBABLY EVEN **COUNTED** ON IT. IN FACT... HOW DID HE KNOW THEY WERE HIDDEN IN THE HOUSE?
HE DIDN'T. HE COULDN'T HAVE.

THAT'S RIGHT. BESIDES MARIAH, THE ONLY ONE WHO KNEW... WAS **YOU!**
HOLD UP, I WANTED YOU TO TAKE THE BLOODY THINGS TO THE CHIEF!

SO YOU SAY. BUT SUPPOSE, JUST SUPPOSE, STICKLEBACK'S **RIGHT**? THAT LIME IS IN ON THIS CITY FATHERS CONSPIRACY?
WE'D BE HANDING HIM OUR EVIDENCE AGAINST HIM ON A PLATE!
IF THERE **IS** A BLEEDIN' CONSPIRACY IN THE FIRST PLACE! DON'T YOU GET IT, BOSS? THAT MAGGOT'S GETTING INTO YOUR HEAD!

SO IF LIME'S CLEAN, THEN YOU'RE **STILL** THE ONLY ONE WHO KNEW ABOUT THE PAPERS. ONE WAY OR THE OTHER, WHERE DOES THAT LEAVE YOU?
WITH A NUTTER FOR A BOSS AND MY HEAD SPINNIN'!

YOU THINK THIS IS A JOKE?
YOU THINK THIS FUNNY?
MY WIFE — MY CHILDREN — ARE DEAD! DEAD! YOU HEAR ME!

GET SODDIN' WELL OFF ME! I DON'T WANT T'FIGHT YOU!

YOU THINK I DON'T FEEL IT? I AIN'T MADE OF STONE! I KNEW YOUR MISSUS — YOUR KIDDIES! YOU THINK I'D HURT 'EM?
YOU'VE GOT TO GET HOLD OF YOURSELF! THAT CROOK- BACKED CRIPPLE'S GOT YOU TURNIN' ON YOUR OWN!

I...
... YOU'RE RIGHT, LEN, I'M SORRY.

WHERE YOU GOIN'?
AWAY FROM ALL THIS. I NEED TO THINK.

COME BACK TO TH'YARD WITH ME. CUPPA TEA AND A KIP WILL CLEAR YOUR HEAD RIGHT UP. WE GET YOU SORTED, BACK TO NORMAL.

NOTHING'S EVER GOING TO BE NORMAL AGAIN. GOOD-BYE, LEN.

GOODBYE...

'AND THAT WAS THE LAST YOU SAW OF HIM?'

YES, SIR.
PITY. FOR ALL HIS FAULTS AND TEA-STAINED SKIN, HE WAS A GOOD MAN. I MAY EVEN HAVE CONSIDERED RECRUITING HIM.

THEN HE WOULDN'T HAVE BEEN A GOOD MAN NO MORE, WOULD HE?
ENOUGH OF YOUR IMPUDENCE! BEY CANNOT BE PERMITTED TO ROAM FREE. HE IS AN UNSTABLE ELEMENT AT THIS TENUOUS TIME.

LET ME HANDLE IT, SIR. I'LL BRING HIM IN.
TOO LATE FOR THAT. DETECTIVE BEY'S FATE IS NO LONGER IN MY HANDS.

'I HAVE GIVEN THE INSTRUCTION. THE RUNES HAVE BEEN CAST.

'THERE IS TO BE A HARVEST...

'... A BLACK DOG IS TO BE SET UPON HIM!'

AND TO YOU, VALENTINE — DO YOU GIVE YOURSELF TO MARIAH, IN LOVE AND LABOUR? INVITE HER INTO YOUR LIFE AND SOUL IN ORDER THAT SHE MAY FULLY KNOW YOU?

DO YOU VOW TO REMAIN STEADFAST AND FAITHFUL, TO HONOUR AND CHERISH HER, IN SICKNESS AND IN HEALTH, FORSAKING ALL OTHERS, IN THE EYES OF THE LORD, FOR AS LONG AS YOU BOTH SHALL LIVE?

I DO.

THEN LET NO MAN PUT ASUNDER WHAT HAS BEEN JOINED HERE THIS DAY. IN THE NAME OF THE ALMIGHTY FATHER, SON AND HOLY SPIRIT, I PRONOUNCE YOU MAN AND WIFE...

MARIAH...

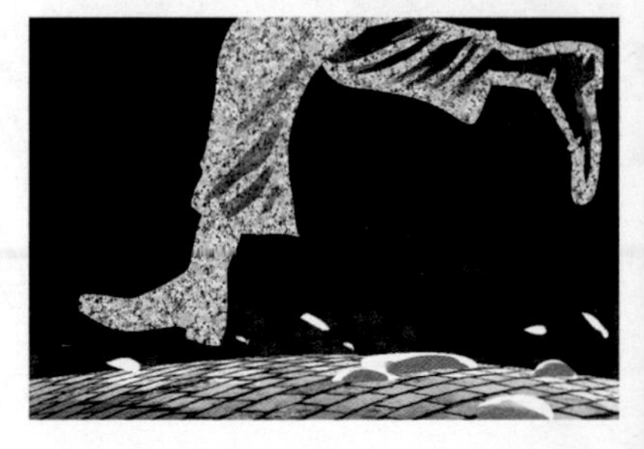

OH GOD... GOD... THIS ISN'T **RIGHT!**

MY SON?
FATHER, FORGIVE ME. I'M SORRY. I MEANT NO DISRESPECT.

NONE WAS TAKEN BY ME. NOR **HE**, WHOSE HOUSE THIS IS. I DO NOT THINK HE WOULD HAVE A PROBLEM WITH YOU SPEAKING HIS NAME HERE.
YOU SEEM TROUBLED, MY SON.
MY WIFE... MY CHILDREN... DIED TONIGHT. THERE WAS A FIRE... I... WASN'T THERE... I COULDN'T SAVE THEM.
IT SHOULD HAVE BEEN **ME!** WHY WASN'T IT ME?
PERHAPS BECAUSE IT WAS NOT YOUR TIME. GOD STILL HAS WORK FOR YOU.
I KNOW THE PAIN IS ALL-CONSUMING NOW. THOSE LEFT BEHIND ARE ALWAYS BOUND TO SUFFER MOST. DO NOT GRIEVE BUT **REJOICE**. THE LORD HAS CALLED THEM TO HIM. THEY DWELL IN PARADISE NOW.
NO, YOU'RE WRONG...
'... THE LORD HAD NO PART IN THIS.'

I HAVE MADE AN ENEMY OF AN EVIL MAN AND MY FAMILY HAS SUFFERED FOR IT. HE SOUGHT TO DEBILITATE ME, STAB AT MY SOUL BY DESTROYING THOSE I LOVE. THAT WAS AN ERROR.
HE HAS STRIPPED ME OF MY MORAL MEDIAN, MY LOVE, MY GUIDE. WHAT I VALUE THE MOST HAS BEEN **SEARED** FROM ME.

I HAVE NOTHING LEFT TO **FEAR**. NOTHING LEFT TO **LIVE** FOR.

DO NOT ABANDON THE LORD, MY SON. ALL THINGS HAPPEN TO HIS PURPOSE, THOUGH WE MAY NOT PERCEIVE IT AT THE TIME. HOLD TRUE AND HAVE FAITH.

EMBRACE HIS LOVE—

KHHSSAA!

AAHH!
KHSSS!

NO!
UH-HH-UH—

SKLUTCH!

WHAT MANNER OF MAN ARE YOU? ANOTHER OF HIS **CARNIVAL FREAKS**? DOESN"T HE DARE SOIL HIS HANDS HIMSELF?
HGRRRR!

HSSSA!

NYAHH!
WHUNNG!

WHUDDAM!

IS THAT IT? IS THAT ALL YOU HAVE FOR ME?

HGGRRR!
COME ON THEN, MONSTER! DO YOUR WORST!

BDAM!
BDAM!
RIEEE!

BDAM!
BDAM!
BDAM!
GGRRII!

NASTY BLEEDERS! HARDER TO GET RID OF THAN THE CLAP!

LEN? WHAT'RE YOU DOING HERE?
SAVING YOUR LIFE, BOSS. FOR THE MOMENT, ANYWAY.
WE'RE BOTH DEAD MEN NOW!

The Monarch of the Glen
Y'BARKIN' UP THE WRONG TREE, BOSS. THAT... THING WASN'T ONE OF STICKLEBACK'S CREATURES.

IT WAS ONE OF OURS — THE CITY FATHERS.
WHAT? YOU MEAN... YOU LIED TO ME? YOU'RE IN WITH THEM? IS THAT WHAT YOU'RE SAYING?

I'M SAYIN' SIT DOWN, Y'IDIOT! THEY'VE EYES AN' EARS ALL OVER THE SHOP! THEY WANT YOU GONE, AN' ME AN' ALL NOW! WE'VE GOT TO PUT OUR HEADS TOGETHER IF WE WANT TO LIVE THROUGH THIS!

I'VE NOTHING LEFT TO LIVE FOR!
SPEAK FOR Y'SELF!

ARE THEY RESPONSIBLE? DID THEY MURDER MY FAMILY? SET A FIRE TO MY LIFE?
IN ALL HONESTY? I DUNNO. AFTER LIME ORDERED THE BLACK DOG SET ON YOU, I DUNNO WHAT TO THINK...

SO THE CROOK-BACK VILLAIN WAS RIGHT ALL ALONG. LIME **IS** IN ON THIS... WHO ARE THEY, THESE CITY FATHERS?
I DUNNO IT ALL, I'M JUST A LITTLE FISH, BUT FROM WHAT I LEARNT THEY'VE BEEN AROUND A THOUSAND YEARS OR MORE. THEY BUILT THIS CITY, RUN IT, AN' OWN IT. THEY'RE IN THE BRICKS AN' MORTAR, SHIT AN' SAWDUST.
NO MATTER WHO THOUGHT THEY WERE IN CHARGE — ROMANS, NORMANS, HANOVERIANS — THEY'VE ALWAYS BEEN THE POWER **BEHIND** THE POWER. LONDON BELONGS TO THEM.
'THEY'RE AN ORDER, LIKE DRUIDS, MONKS OR MASONS. ALL HOODS AN' CHANTIN' AND Y'TROUSER LEG AT HALF-MAST.
'THEY'RE ALL ABOUT MAINTAINING THE BALANCE, WHETHER IT'S BETWEEN RICH AN' POOR, LAW AND LAWLESSNESS, POVERTY AN' PROSPERITY. THEY PLAY BOTH THE CARROT AN' THE STICK.'
HOW DID YOU GET INVOLVED?
I STARTED OUT AS A BEAT COPPER, LIKE YOU. SEEMED LIKE EVERYONE WAS ON THE SHILL AN' GRIFT BACK THEN. BLOKES I KNEW WERE TAKIN' BACKHANDERS AND BUNGS T'LOOK THE OTHER WAY OR CRACK THE ODD HEAD.
'I DIDN'T HOLD WITH IT. I WAS BROUGHT UP A GOOD BAPTIST. WHEN I TRIED STICKIN' ME OAR IN, I GOT THE TAR WHALED OUT'VE ME.
'I WAS CONTEMPLATIN' CHUCKIN' IT IN WHEN LIME CAME CALLIN'. HE TALKED 'BOUT THE FATHERS, HOW THEY WERE CLEANIN' UP THE CITY, BRINGIN' BACK OLD-FASHIONED VALUES.'

THEM WHO JOINED WERE LOOKED ON FAVOURABLE, GIVEN A LEG UP. NOTHIN' DODGY, JUST A NUDGE.
WELL, IT WAS THAT OR THE WORK-HOUSE, SO WITH THE OLD MAN'S CONSENT I SIGNED UP.

'WAS A WEIRD T'DO. RITES AN' RITUALS AN' FUNNY HANDSHAKES. IT'S ALL BASED AROUND THE OAK TREE F'SOME REASON, SPLIT UP INTO BRANCHES THAT HANDLE ALL SORTS OF GUFF...
'... LAW AN' ORDER, THE CLERGY, COMMERCE AN' CRIME...'

CRIME?
THEY FIGURE THE BEST WAY TO LIMIT THE SPREAD O'VILLAINY IS TO BE PART OF IT. THE RANK AN' FILE, THE DIPPERS, FOOTPADS AN' CRACKSMEN, DON'T KNOW IT BUT THEIR MINDERS DO.

WHICH'S WHY STICKLEBACK WANTS TO UNDERMINE THEM. THEY'RE EATING INTO HIS TRADE.
MORE'N THAT. LIME WAS RIGHT, THEY'RE USIN' THEIR INFLUENCE T'RUN THE CITY, BUT THEIR OWN WAY. DIPPIN' THEIR SPOONS IN THAT GRAVY PROVED NIGH IRRESISTIBLE.

'THE ROT'S SET IN AN' RIFE. MONEY EARMARKED F'GOOD WORKS GETS POCKETED. YOUNG GIRLS ARE PRESSED INTO ALL MANNER OF PERVERTED PROCEEDINGS...

'MURDERS ARE A MATTER OF COURSE, NO MATTER WHAT YOUR STATION.'

YET YOU DID NOTHING!
HOW COULD I? THEY'RE BLOODY WELL **EVERYWHERE!** Y'KNOW WHAT THEY DID TO THYNNE!

I THOUGHT THAT WAS STICKLEBACK'S KILL?

S'WHAT THEY **WANT** YOU T'THINK! ANY OF THEIR SHITTY DOIN'S COMES TO LIGHT, THEY BLAME **HIM**. HE'S NOT GONNA JUMP UP AN' DEFEND HIMSELF, NOW IS HE?
EXCEPT EVEN **HE'S** HAD ENOUGH. THAT'S WHY HE DRAGGED ME INTO THIS.

WE CAN'T LINGER. WE GOTTA LEAVE THE CITY. TELL THE PAPERS UP IN MANCHESTER, OR GLASGOW, GOD FORBID. EVEN THE FATHERS' REACH AIN'T THAT LONG.
IF WE CAN LIE LOW 'TIL TOMORROW NIGHT WE SHOULD GET AWAY CLEAN AN' CLEAR. THEY'LL BE CELEBRATIN' THE MIDSUMMER SOLSTICE. IT'S A BIG BASH, EVERYONE GOES — THERE'LL HARDLY BE ANY OF THEIR SPIES ON WATCH.

I WANT TO SEE IT.
EH? NO... NO, I DON'T RECOMMEND IT. IT'S OUR ONLY CHANCE TO GET CLEAR—
I DON'T GIVE A TOSS **WHAT** YOU THINK! YOU **OWE** ME! JUST TELL ME WHERE IT IS — I'LL GO ALONE IF NEED BE!

YOU WOULDN'T LAST FIVE MINUTES. YOU'D NEED ONE OF THESE FOR STARTERS.

GIVE ME YOURS.
UH-UH, I'LL BE USIN' IT. WE'LL GET YOU ANOTHER ONE.
'WE'?

Y'DON'T THINK I'M GONNA LET ME GUV'NOR WALK INTO HELL ALONE, DO YOU?
JUST ONE THING, THOUGH... ARE WE STILL MATES?

YOU'RE A SOLID COPPER, A NOBLE FRIEND AND A GOOD MAN, LEN CHIPPS.

I'LL HAVE 'EM PUT THAT ON ME HEADSTONE!

IT'S ON THEN?
OH YES INDEEDY...

THERE IS NO POSSIBLE WAY THIS IS GOING TO WORK!

REALLY? WHAT GIVES YOU THAT IDEA, PRAY TELL?
IF IT WAS DOWN T'ME, WE'D BE HALFWAY UP BEN NEVIS BY NOW. SO, IF YOU'VE A BETTER PLAN FOR SNEAKING INTO THE LION'S DEN INCOGNITO, I'M ALL EARS!

YOU LOOK ABSURD.
'LEAST I'M NOT THE ONE WEARIN' A DRESS AGAIN! 'SIDES, WHILE THEY'RE ALL BUSY CHUCKLIN' AT ME, IT WON'T OCCUR TO 'EM WE'RE UP TO NO GOOD!

SPEAKIN' OF WHICH — WE'RE GREATLY OBLIGED FOR YOUR HOSPITALITY, SIR WILLIAM. YOUR FROCK FITS MY FRIEND HERE A TREAT!

NOW, I'LL JUST RELIEVE YOU OF THIS SHINY GEE-GAW AN' WE'LL BE ON OUR WAY!

WILL THIS WORK?
TRUTH? I THINK IT'S DOOMED FROM THE START AN' WE'RE BOTH GOING TO DIE STRANGE AN' 'ORRIBLE DEATHS!
HOWEVER, ON THE PLUS SIDE, THEY'RE AN ARROGANT BUNCH WHO THINK NOTHIN' CAN TOUCH 'EM.
THESE THINGS HERE ARE LIKE THE KEYS TO THE KINGDOM, NO QUESTIONS ASKED...

'... IF YOU'VE GOT 'EM, YOU'RE IN!'
GOOD EVENING, GENTLEMEN. ENTER FREELY AND UNAFRAID.
THERE ARE NO RULES HERE SAVE ONE — LET DO WHAT THOU WILT BE THE WHOLE OF THE LAW!
GOOD GOD!
THERE'S LITTLE GOD HERE, GUV, OF ANY SORT OR MANNER.
ALSO, WORD TO TH'WISE: DON'T TOUCH THE BOOZE. IT'LL BE DOSED WITH ANYTHIN' FROM ABSINTHE TO OPIUM. THAT'S HOW COME THIS LOT ARE SO ARSE-HOLED.
HOW DID IT COME TO THIS?

POWER'S A TEMPTIN' PUDDIN'. Y'START OFF MEANIN' WELL, DOIN' THE RIGHT THING... A DIP OF Y'SPOON FOR Y'SELF NOW AND THEN, NO HARM DONE. 'CEPT SOON, IT AIN'T ENOUGH. YOU WANT THE WHOLE PIE, DISH AN' ALL.
IT'S A SLIPPERY SLOPE. EASY T'SET FOOT ON, HARDER T'GET OFF.

YOU DID IT.
YEAH, WELL, I'M EXPECTIN' TO BE FLOATIN' FACE-DOWN IN THE THAMES COME THE END OF THE NIGHT, SO LET'S NOT GET AHEAD OF OURSELVES, EH?

SEE ANYONE YOU RECOGNISE?
THIS BUN-FIGHT'S FOR THE RANK AND FILE. TITS, TARTS AN' TODDIES, IN THANKS FOR THEIR DIRTY DEEDS.
THE MAIN PLAYERS KEEP THEIR BUSINESS BEHIND CLOSED DOORS.

HOWEVER, IT LOOKS LIKE OUR LUCK'S IN! SEE OVER THERE? THAT'S LIME!

HOW CAN YOU TELL?

I'D RECOGNISE THE OLD DEVIL ANYWHERE—

HE'S WEARING HIS FAVOURITE PARTY PIECE!

WHAT'S DOWN HERE?
I... I DON'T KNOW.
ONLY ONE WAY TO FIND OUT. BUT FIRST THINGS FIRST — ENOUGH WITH THE CHARADES.
THANK GAWD FOR THAT! I WAS SWEATIN' LIKE A PIG IN GRAVY!
THAT'S ODD...
... IS IT ME...
... OR IS IT GETTIN' WARMER?
WHAT... IS... THIS?
I DUNNO, BUT I DON'T LIKE IT! WE SHOULD GO! NOW!

GHUKK!
LEN!
HEH!
THUS PERISH ALL TRAITORS!
LIME! YOU BASTARD!
ALTHOUGH IN YOUR CASE, VALENTINE, PERHAPS YOUR DEMISE SHOULD BE PUNCTUATED WITH SOMETHING A TAD MORE PROSAIC?
AH, I HAVE IT...
'... ABANDON ALL HOPE YE WHO ENTER HERE!'
NOK NOK
EVENIN', SON. HAVE Y'HEARD THE WORD OF THE LORD?
SALVATION ARMY

DETECTIVE VALENTINE BEY HAS DISCOVERED THAT SECRET SOCIETY THE CITY FATHERS ARE BEHIND MUCH OF LONDON'S ORGANISED CRIME. AT ONE OF THEIR GATHERINGS, HE CONFRONTS HIS SUPERIOR, CHIEF CONSTABLE DELIUS LIME...
COME ON THEN, YOU OLD BASTARD! FINISH IT! THAT'S WHAT YOU WANT, ISN'T IT?
YOU HAD MY FAMILY MURDERED — SAW MY FRIEND KILLED — DO IT YOURSELF THIS TIME! GET SOME BLOOD ON YOUR HANDS!
I CAN'T TAKE CREDIT FOR ALL YOUR WOES, BUT I'D BE DELIGHTED TO PUT YOU DOWN, DEAR BOY. YOU SHOULD KNOW, YOU'RE NOT THE FIRST MAN I'VE MURDERED AND CERTAINLY WON'T BE THE LAST.
HOWEVER, I WILL TAKE A CERTAIN SATISFACTION IN BLOWING YOUR INSOLENT BRAINS OUT. AND I THANK GOD I WON'T HAVE TO LOOK AT THAT RIDICULOUS MOUSTACHE EVER AGAIN—
YAAHH!
WHA—?
BDAM
UKK!
MY WIFE LIKED THIS MOUSTACHE!
GHTDDIMOFFME! GHEDDIMOFF!
HHH...

GUK!
YOU LITTLE SHIT!

FOR GOD'S SAKE, HOW CAN YOU **DO** THIS? YOU'RE SUPPOSED TO **PROTECT** PEOPLE, NOT **PREY** ON THEM!

PEOPLE! LET ME TELL YOU ALL ABOUT PEOPLE, SONNY JIM! TO A MAN, ALL THE GREAT BRITISH PUBLIC WANT TO DO IS EAT, FIGHT, FORNICATE AND DEFECATE — USUALLY IN THAT ORDER!
I WASTED DECADES OF MY LIFE SERVING THIS DAMN CITY, AND FOR WHAT? A HANDSHAKE AND A GOLD WATCH? A SLOW DECLINE INTO TEDIUM AND INCONTINENCE? NOT IF I HAVE MY WAY!

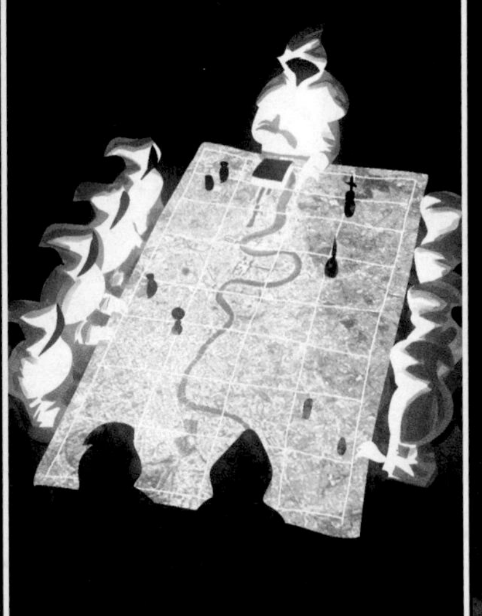
'THAT'S WHY A GROUP OF US LIT A FIRE UNDER THIS LOT. I MEAN, WHAT'S THE POINT OF BELONGING TO A SECRET SOCIETY IF YOU DON'T DO **SECRET THINGS**, EH?
'THEY WERE A STRANGE, FUSTY BUNCH WHEN I WAS RECRUITED. ALL BELLS, CHANTS AND DANCING AROUND MAY-POLES. THEY WERE EVEN TRYING TO DO GOOD WORKS, INFLUENCE THE SUBTLE MECHANISMS OF THE CITY, TINKERING WITH A LITTLE SOCIAL ENGINEERING...

'YOU KNOW WHAT HAPPENED? BUGGER ALL!
'THEY TRIED HELPING THE PEOPLE OF THIS FAIR CITY OUT OF THE FILTH THEY WALLOWED IN, EXCEPT THEY JUMPED STRAIGHT BACK IN! THEY DON'T **WANT** TO BE SAVED! THEY **LIKE** LIVING IN SHIT! IT'S ALL THEY KNOW!'

SO THAT MAKES IT ALL RIGHT FOR YOU TO EXPLOIT THEM AT EVERY TURN? BLEED THIS PLACE LIKE A TICK, SO YOU AND THE REST OF THE CITY FATHERS CAN LIVE THE HIGH LIFE?
ME, A CITY FATHER?
HA HA HA! TO THINK I WAS WORRIED! YOU DON'T HAVE THE FAINTEST INKLING, DO YOU?

BRING HIM!

AS UNLIKELY AS IT SOUNDS, YOU AND I ARE NOT ENTIRELY DISSIMILAR, BEY. I WAS A YOUNG OFFICER ONCE AND WITNESSED THE GRAPHIC BASENESS OF MANKIND FIRST HAND.
THE MUNDANE BRUTALITY OF IT. THE OBSCENE, THE UNSPEAKABLE, THE BIZARRE. EVERY DAY ANOTHER VILE REVELATION OR PITIFUL TRAGEDY...

... I THOUGHT I'D SEEN IT ALL.
W-WHAT ARE THEY DOING?

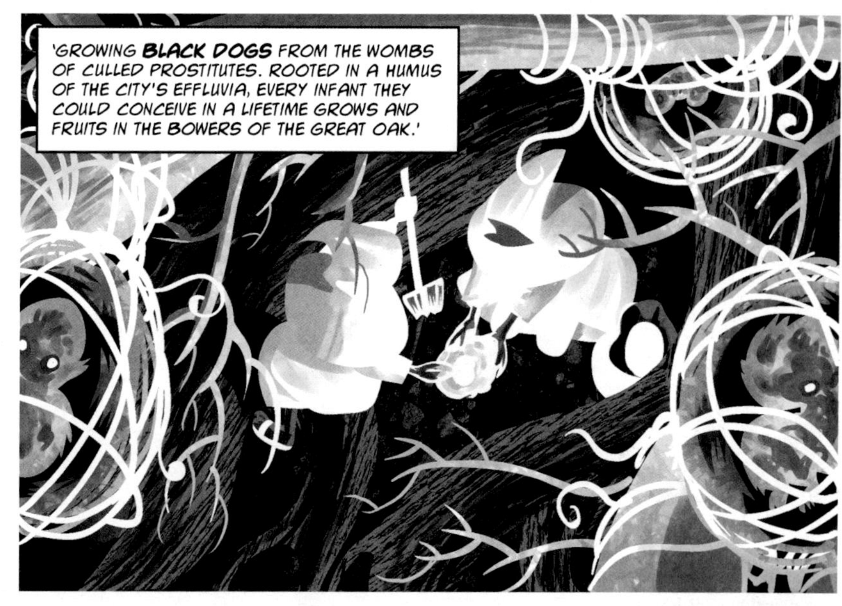
'GROWING BLACK DOGS FROM THE WOMBS OF CULLED PROSTITUTES. ROOTED IN A HUMUS OF THE CITY'S EFFLUVIA, EVERY INFANT THEY COULD CONCEIVE IN A LIFETIME GROWS AND FRUITS IN THE BOWERS OF THE GREAT OAK.'

RATHER LIKE MISTLETOE, REALLY. IT'S ACTUALLY VERY PRETTY.
YOU'RE INSANE.

POSSIBLY. HOWEVER, WHERE THE SECRET HISTORY OF THIS FAIR CITY IS CONCERNED, IT'S AS MUCH ABOUT MAGIC AS MADNESS. TAKE THIS PAIR, FOR INSTANCE—
OH MY GOD!

NO, NOT GOD — OR GODS — ONLY MEN, ONCE...
... BROTHERS OF WOMB AND WOOD. GOG AND MAGOG.
ARE YOU GROTESQUES RESPONSIBLE FOR ALL THIS HORROR-SHOW?
WITH REGRET, WE ARE... AND WE ARE NOT. AGES PAST, WE SACRIFICED OUR FLESH AND SOULS TO STAND THE LONG WATCH OVER THIS DWELLING PLACE, AS WE DID IN OUR WARM DAYS.
THE GREAT OAK IS ROOTED TO THE WORLD AND THE CITY TO THE OAK. WE ARE GRAFTED UPON THEM BOTH, SO WE MAY KNOW THEIR MIND AND THEY OURS.

WE NURTURE THE MEAT AND MARROW OF THE LAND ABOVE. EACH LIFE AND THE MEANDERING PATH IT TAKES IS BUT A ROOT, SHOOT AND LIMB ON THE BODY OF THE GREAT OAK.
EXCEPT THE DRUID PRIESTS WHO BOUND US HERE WERE FEY AND FICKLE. THEY REALISED WHAT POWERS OF GOOD FORTUNE AND FORECAST WE MIGHT WIELD AND SO SHACKLED OUR SOULS WITH MAJIKS.
WE HAVE BEEN MADE TO DO SUCH THINGS AS TO SHAME A WARRIOR'S HONOUR. WE YEARN FOR THE EARTH TO CLAIM US, SO THAT WE MAY FINALLY FIND OUR EASE.
THERE IS ONE WHO WILL COME TO SET US **FREE** — BUT YOU ARE NOT HE, VALENTINE BEY. YOU ARE DESTINED TO WALK ANOTHER, DARKER WINDING WAY.
ACTUALLY, HE'S NOT. HE'S FOR THE CHOP.
THEY... KNEW MY NAME?
IT'S THEIR LITTLE PARLOUR TRICK. BUT WHAT'S IN A NAME, EH?
HELLO, DELIUS. IT'S BEEN QUITE A WHILE, HASN'T IT?
EH?
WHAT THE DEVIL - ?
SAY MY NAME, YOU MAKE ME REAL!
SALLY ARMY

GOOD GOD... NO... NOT YOU! IT'S **IMPOSSIBLE**! YOU'RE DEAD! YOU AND ALL THOSE BLOODY SEPOYS! I SAW YOU **DIE**!
OH, THEY ARE. POOR BRAVE BUGGERS. BOOT'S ON THE OTHER FOOT NOW THOUGH, YOU BUTCHERIN' BASTARD!

BLACK BOB! LIGHT 'EM UP!
RIGHTCHOARE, BOSS!

NO! YOU'RE DEAD!
DEAD!

NYAAAHHHH!

GIIAAAA!
AAAHHH!
GAAAHHH!

THUS PERISH ALL TYRANTS!
SALVATION ARMY

MMM...
SMASHING!
SALVATION ARMY

ALL RIGHT, BOB, EASE OFF. I'M SWEATING COBS AS IT IS.

HHNNHH...
VAL, MY OLD CHINA! YOU'VE DONE ME A FINE SERVICE T'DAY, BOY! I WON'T FORGET IT!

KOFF! KOFF!
H-HOW DID YOU FIND ME?
OH, YOU KNOW ME. I GOT M'RESOURCES. AN' AS F'THEM UPSTAIRS, THEY'RE HAVIN' A BIT OF A LIE DOWN COURTESY OF A CERTAIN SOMETHIN' WE LIFTED OFF ONE OF HER MAJESTY'S LOCOMOTIVES...

'... THOUGH BY THE FACES THEY WERE PULLIN' THEY CAN'T LIKE THE TASTE O'MUSTARD MUCH!'

THEY'RE DEAD?
I HOPE SO.
SALVATION ARMY
THIS... IT'S BARBARIC! HOW CAN YOU LIVE WITH YOURSELF?
IT BECOMES EASIER OVER TIME. AND THEY WEREN'T NICE PEOPLE. TRUST ME, I KNOW GOOD FROM BAD.
IF YOU KNEW ABOUT LIME ALL ALONG, WHY WAIT UNTIL NOW TO STRIKE?
WHY MURDER SO MANY, WHEN... OH... I SEE...
IT WAS YOU, WASN'T IT? SET FIRE TO MY HOUSE, MY WIFE, MY CHILDREN! YOU DID IT TO GET ME ON THE CASE, NOT FOR LIME BUT FOR THIS PLACE!
WELL NOW, YOU'RE CERTAINLY EARNING YOUR CORN AS COPPER TODAY!
DO YOU KNOW WHAT YOU'VE DONE?
DO YOU?
UHTT!
WHAT I HAD TO DO.

UHHHH...
FOR WHAT IT'S WORTH, I'M SORRY, SON...

... BUT IT'LL PASS.

YOU! YOU ARE THE ONE!
I'LL BE DAMNED... YOU'RE REAL, WHATEVER YOU ARE.

WE ARE YOUR FATHERS BY MYRIAD TINY TWISTS OF FATE, OF CAUSALS, COINCIDENCES AND SEEMINGLY RANDOM ACTS OF LUCK AND LUST.
NO, YOU'RE NOT! I AM NEITHER MAN NOR MONSTER'S CATS-PAW!
WE SHEPHERDED YOUR FAMILY LINE TO THIS VERY MOMENT. THE WAY YOUR MOTHER LIVED, THE METALS AND POISONS IN THE AIR AND WATER SHE CONSUMED, WARPING YOU WITHIN HER — WE MADE YOU!
YOUR DESTINY AWAITS! THE CITY IS YOURS! NOW GIVE US WHAT WE CRAVE! GIVE US RELEASE!

BOB, GET YOUR UNDEAD ARSE OVER HERE!
YES, GUV.
SALVATION ARMY

BURN 'EM!

'BURN IT ALL.

'BRING IT ALL TO ASH AND THEN BURN IT AGAIN.'

FROM THIS DAY FORWARD, LONDON BELONGS TO **ME**!

ENGLAND'S GLORY

Script: Ian Edginton
Art: D'Israeli
Letters: Ellie De Ville

Originally published in *2000 AD* Progs 2008 1567-1577

LONDON:
GET OUT OF THE WAY!
OI! WATCH Y'BLEEDIN' STEP!
GONE! THANK GOD!
GIT AHT OV IT, Y'PISS 'OUND!
BLEEDIN' CHEEK!

GOD'S TEETH!
NUAHH!
SHRIPPP

HUF!
HUF!
HUF!
UH!
SORRY, FIDO, BUT NEEDS MUST...

CHRIST ALMIGHTY!

COME ON, COME ON...

GUHK!

HTTT...

GOOD BOYS!

NOW PLAY DEAD!

Y'GAVE ME A GOOD RUN FOR M'MONEY THERE, SON, BUT THIS WAS ONLY EVER GONNA WIND UP ONE WAY.

A THING O'BEAUTY AN' NO MISTAKE!

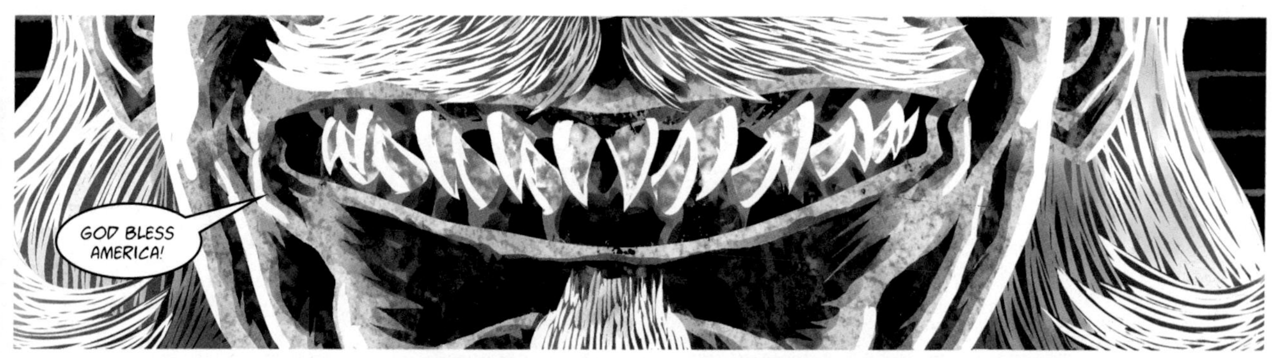
GOD BLESS AMERICA!

MAY YOU BE CURSED T'LIVE IN INTERESTIN' TIMES. THAT'S HOW THE SAYIN' GOES, ISN'T IT?
WELL, I COULD DO WITH BEING CURSED, 'CAUSE RIGHT NOW I'M BORED T'THE TEATS!
SO LET'S GET ON WITH IT. WHAT'S THE GOOD WORD, MY LOVELIES?

MR TICKLE?
SAME AS EVER, BOSS. ALL TICKETY-BOO.
THE LASCARS AT THE DOCKS WERE SKIMMIN' MORE THAN THEIR PERMITTED PERCENTAGE, SO I HAD BLACK BOB AND TONGA REMIND THEM OF THE PREVIOUSLY AGREED ARRANGEMENT.

WE HELPED 'EM WITH THEIR COUNTIN'.
HEH! HEH! SNIP SNIP! HAH!

GAY JOHN?
TRUE TO THEIR WORD, THE ARABIANS' NEW BATCH OF HASHISH IS OF PEERLESS QUALITY, AND ONLY FOR AN EXTRA FARTHING ON THE BUSHEL.

MISS SCARLET?
BUSINESS IS ON THE UP, THOUGH WE'RE GETTING SOME OCCASIONAL GRIEF FROM A SUITED AND BOOTED BRUTE WHO LIKES TO ROUGH UP THE GIRLS.

HE'S MATES WITH SOME WEEDY SCOTTISH SAW-BONES. I'VE ASKED MR PEEPERS AND MR LUG TO LOOK INTO IT.
HIDE
AND SEEK!

SO **THAT'S** IT? THAT'S TICKETY-BOO?
'FRAID SO, OLD DARLING. SINCE YOU DISPENSED WITH THE **CITY FATHERS** AND THEIR ILL-GOTTEN ILK, THE NASTY AND NEFARIOUS OF THIS FAIR CITY HAVE BEEN MOST HAPPY TO FOLLOW YOUR BANNER.

Y'SEE, THERE'S THE RUB. COMPARED TO THE FATHERS' DRACONIAN DEALINGS, THEY CONSIDER ME A **SOFT TOUCH**...
... THAT I'LL TOLERATE THE LASCARS DIPPING MY POCKET, OR THE ARABIANS HIKING THEIR PRICES FOR THE KIND OF HASH THEY SHOULD'VE BEEN SELLING TO **US** ANYWAY!
OR THAT A BRUTE GETS AWAY WITH BEATING UPON MY GIRLS, WHEN HE SHOULD HAVE BEEN GUTTED AND ROLLED THE FIRST TIME HE RAISED A HAND!
LOVE...

DON'T 'LOVE' ME! DON'T PROFESS TO KNOW ME! WE ARE NOT EQUALS! I AM ALL YOUR MASTER! YOU EACH WOULD DO WELL TO REMEMBER THAT!
AAAHHH!
TELL THOSE MONGREL ARABIANS I'LL PAY THE OLD PRICE, OR THEY'LL BE PUTTING OUT FIRES ON THEIR CHILDREN'S BACKS!
AND AS FOR THE LASCARS — HALF THEIR RATE AND CUT THE COCK AND BALLS OFF EVERY THIRD MAN!
YAH! YAH! YAH!
'THEY'VE FORGOTTEN WHAT IT IS TO BE AFRAID, SO I SHALL REACQUAINT THEM!'
THERE, NOW. DRY YOUR EYES. NO HARM DONE.

CASHOOOM!
WHAT... WHAT ARE THEY?
EXPECTED. SORT OF.
SIR GALAHAD
SIR LAUNCELOT
SIR GAWAIN
GOOD MORNING. CAN I HELP YOU?

GO! GO! LOOK LIVELY!

STAND STILL! DON'T MOVE!
SIR GALAHAD
COME NOW, SERGEANT. WHERE ARE YOUR MANNERS?
I DO APOLOGISE. BEING COOPED IN THOSE KETTLES PLAYS HAVOC WITH THEIR GOOD HUMOUR, ESPECIALLY WHEN THEY'VE ALL EATEN SPROUTS FOR LUNCH.
MR STICKLEBACK, I PRESUME?
I AM HE.
MY NAME IS **ALEXANDER ASHENDEN**. I REPRESENT A CERTAIN... **AGENCY** OF HER MAJESTY'S GOVERNMENT.
AND NOW, SIR, SO DO YOU!

S'PPOSE Y'DON'T HAVE T'BE MAD T'WORK 'ERE... BUT IT HELPS, EH?
Bethlem Royal Hospital Lambeth
OUR PRESENCE HERE MAKES IT EASIER TO OBSCURE AND OBFUSCATE THE SECRETS OF STATE AMIDST THE FOG OF MADNESS. WHERE ELSE ARE FACT, FICTION AND FANTASY SO READILY BLURRED?
YEAH, WELL, IT LOOKS LIKE THE LUNATICS HAVE TAKEN OVER THE ASYLUM T'ME, CHUM.
WHERE ARE MY PEOPLE, BY THE WAY?
SAFE AND WELL. FOR NOW.
AH, MORE VEILED THREATS, EH? YOU'RE GONNA HAVE T'DO BETTER'N THAT, SON, IF Y'WANT ME T'TAKE Y'SERIOUSLY.
I AM BEING DEATHLY SERIOUS!
WELL, IT AIN'T WORKIN'.
LOOK, I BET THE LINE YOU'VE BEEN TOLD T'FEED ME IS THAT HER MAJESTY'S GOVERNMENT REQUESTS THE PLEASURE OF ME AN' MY COLOURFUL COMPATRIOTS T'DO A LITTLE JOB IN EXCHANGE F'PARDONS ALL ROUND OR SOME SUCH, AM I RIGHT?
POSSIBLY...
'CEPT WE DON'T WANNA BE PARDONED! WE'RE HAPPY AS PIGS IN MUCK THE WAY WE ARE. 'SIDES, WE DON'T EXACTLY BELONG IN POLITE SOCIETY, NOW DO WE?
YOU BANG US UP, WE'LL GET OUT, REST ASSURED. WE'LL ALSO BE VERY, VERY ANGRY.
SEE, YOU COME BUSTIN' UP MY GAFF WITH Y'TIN MEN, MAKIN' ME LOOK SMALL IN FRONT OF THE NEIGHBOURS, HOPIN' TO HAVE ME QUAKIN' IN MY BOOTS.
ALL YOU'VE DONE, BOY, IS PISS IN MY POCKET AN' THAT AIN'T WISE! YOU THINK Y'CAN THREATEN ME? YOU GOT NO IDEA. YOU GOT FRIENDS, FAMILY, MUM AND DAD? 'CAUSE I GOT A THOUSAND WAYS T'CAUSE YOU GRIEF!

THIS ISN'T GETTING US ANYWHERE—
CHEER UP! TELL Y'WHAT, I'LL DO Y'JOB FOR A PROPER RENUMERATION, NONE O'THIS FAFFIN' ABOUT WITH PARDONS!
THIS IS NOT SUBJECT TO NEGOTIATION—
DRING-DRING!
YES. YES, PROFESSOR, BUT HE...
YES. I UNDERSTAND. VERY GOOD, SIR.

WHAT ARE YOUR TERMS?
I WANT ONE THING — AN HONEST ANSWER TO A SINGLE QUESTION AT A TIME AND PLACE OF MY CHOOSING. TAKE IT OR LEAVE IT.

YES, SIR. IS THAT WISE?
NO... I DIDN'T MEAN....
YES, SIR. YES, I WILL.
VERY WELL. IT'S AGREED.

THOUGHT IT MIGHT BE..

SO WHAT'S THE JIG?

'FIVE DAYS AGO, THERE WAS A ROBBERY AT THE JEWEL HOUSE IN THE TOWER OF LONDON. A SINGLE ITEM WAS STOLEN. A CROWN — **THE JEWEL OF THE SEVEN STARS**.

'A NIGHTWATCHMAN WAS... WELL, MURDERED SEEMS TOO **TAME** A DESCRIPTION. HE WAS **TORN APART** BY THE HANDFUL, RENDERED TO GOBBETS. OF THE CULPRIT'S ENTRY OR EXIT, THERE WAS NO TRACE.

'IT WASN'T ONE OF THE MAJOR ARTICLES OF REGALIA AND VESTMENTS BUT A MINOR PIECE PRESENTED AS A GIFT FROM AN EASTERN POTENTATE FOR ONE OF HER MAJESTY'S BIRTHDAYS.'

NOTHING ELSE WAS TAKEN, SO WE MUST ASSUME THERE WAS SOME ULTERIOR, POSSIBLY **POLITICAL** MOTIVE BEHIND THE THEFT. ESPECIALLY GIVEN THE SPOT OF BOTHER WE'RE HAVING IN THE **EAST** AT PRESENT.
YOU TRIED LOOKIN' FOR IT Y'SELF?
OF COURSE, BUT TO NO AVAIL. HENCE OUR TURNING TO YOURSELVES.

SET A THIEF TO CATCH A THIEF, EH?
QUITE.
ONE SNAG THERE, SQUIRE...

'... YOU'RE ASSUMIN' WHOEVER TOOK IT ONLY 'AD **THIEVERY** IN MIND!'
IS IT THE REAL THING, SHEN? DID THAT SON OF A BITCH PULL A SWITCH?
WE SHALL SEE...
AHHHH...
IT... IS MOST CERTAINLY GENUINE. DO YOU HAVE THE REST OF THE CROWN?
NAH, HE MUSTA DITCHED IT WHEN HE REALISED IT WAS JUST THE BIG-ASS STONE WE WANTED.
THEN OUR ENDEAVOURS ARE STILL AT RISK! FOR THOSE WHO KNOW HOW TO LOOK, THE CROWN LEAVES A **TRAIL** BACK TO US! FIND IT! DESTROY IT! WE DO NOT NEED ANY FURTHER DISTRACTIONS!
HEY, DON'T YOU RILE ME, OLD MAN! JUST REMEMBER WHO'S **IN CHARGE** HERE!

YOU DO YOUR BUSINESS —
ANNIE OAKLEY
SWEETHEART SURESHOT OF THE WEST
BUFFALO BILL CODY'S AUTHENTIC WILD WEST CIRCUS
BULLSEYE
THE HUMAN TARGET
EGG SHEN - CHINESE MYSTIC
— AN' I'LL SEE T'MINE!

I DARE SAY THIS HAS CROSSED YOUR MIND, SIR, SO PRAY FORGIVE MY IMPUDENCE —
— BUT OUR CURRENT CONDITION HAS ALL THE REEK OF A SINISTER **CONTRIVANCE**.
'COURSE IT 'AS. POUND TO A PENNY THEM GOVERNMENT BODS TRIED SUSSIN' IT OUT THEMSELVES AN' GOT THEIR DONNIES BURNT. SO NOW THEY'VE GIVEN **US** THE SHITTY END OF THE STICK T'PLAY WITH.
AND WE TOOK IT?
TOO RIGHT! TRUTH IS, THEY'VE 'ANDED US A GIFT 'ORSE. THEY'VE SET US AFTER THAT CROWN WHAT GOT LIFTED, AN' THAT GIVES US **LEVERAGE**. A SHINY FAVOUR T'KEEP IN ME POCKET FOR A RAINY DAY!
WHAT'S THE GOOD WORD ON THE BAUBLE, FIERY JACK?
SLIM AND NONE, OLD DARLING. MISS SCARLET AND MR TICKLE HAVE BEEN ENQUIRING AFTER OUR USUAL FENCES, ONES WHO'D HANDLE SUCH A HIGH-END GEEGAW.
THE TROTTER BROTHERS, OLD MAN STEPTOE AND HIS IDIOT SON... EVEN FLETCHER AND HIS BRUMAGEM SIDEKICK. ALL NOUGHT, I'M AFRAID. THE ONLY ONES WHO DIDN'T ANSWER OUR SUMMONS IS OUR NEXT PORT OF CALL.
Chetwynd Hayes Notary Public
HMM... THIS DON'T SIT RIGHT. DES KINVIG'S USUALLY FOUR SQUARE AN' SOUND AS A POUND. WE GO BACK AWAYS. HE'S THE LAST 'UN I'D EXPECT T'PULL A FAST ONE...
... STILL DON'T MEAN I'D TRUST 'IM AS FAR AS I COULD SPIT A BRICK.
D. KINVIG, Esq.
Purveyor of Fine Antiquities & Curios
IT'S OPEN...

EASY THERE. LIGHT ON Y'TOES, BOYS, 'SPECIALLY YOU, BLACK BOB —
— AIN'T LIKE DES T'LEAVE HIS LIVELIHOOD ON THE LATCH.

THIS IS ALL VERY QUEER AN' CURIOUS STRANGE...

UM, BOSS? BLOOD!

HERE TOO, IN ABUNDANCE. I THINK THIS WAS OUR CHAP...
I THINK THIS WAS TOO!

HELL, WHUT CAN AH SAY?

SOME GUYS JUST PLUMB GO T'PIECES OVER ME!

AMERICANS! I MIGHT'VE KNOWN! YOU GOT BALLS — METAPHORICALLY SPEAKIN' — AN' I CAN RESPECT THAT. SO 'AND OVER THE BAG AN' YOU MIGHT LEAVE WITH Y'FULL QUOTA OF EYES AND FINGERS!
'COURSE, F'WHAT YOU DONE TO OLD DES THERE, I'D BE JUST AS CONTENT T'SEE YOU END Y'DAYS SQUEEZED OUT THE ARSE-END OF A PIG!
Y'THINK AH DID ALL THIS? YOU DUMB-BASTARD CRIPPLE! YOU GOT NO IDEA WHUT Y'DEALIN' WITH HERE, 'ELSE YOU'D BE SHITTIN' Y'DRAWERS AN' FILLIN' Y'BOOTS!
GHRRRR...
Y'DON'T SCARE ME, CROOKED MAN. SEE, AH GOT Y'DEATH RIGHT HERE — SMOKEY!
MOMMA BRUNG YOU DESSERT! SIC 'EM!
GRRAHH!
GREAT STEAMIN' ARSE'OLES!
BDAM! BDAM!
UP YOURS, UGLY!

WOTCHIT, BOSS!
SKRAKKSH!

THWAK!
BAD BEAR!

MAY I?
BY ALL MEANS, DEAR FELLOW. I SENSE MY BODKIN MAY BE SOMEWHAT INEFFECTUAL IN THIS INSTANCE.

ROUND AND ROUND THE GARDEN, LIKE A TEDDY BEAR...
HRRRGH...

ONE STEP...
TWO STEP...

TICKLE HIM UNDER THERE!
GGHRAAA!

GHRIII....

Y'GODDAMN SONS OF BITCHES! THAT WAS M'BEST BEAR!
NOW ALL AH GOT IS SADDLESCUM AN' REDSKINS!
WE SUPPOSED T'MAKE A **WISH** OR WHAT?
AH.
MUHHH...
NOW **THERE'S** SOMETHIN' Y'DON'T SEE EVERY DAY!

GO GIT 'EM, BOYS!

MY THOUGHTS ENTIRELY! OFF Y'GO, LADS, KICK IN! MAKE GUTS AN' GOBBETS OF 'EM ALL!

MOST KIND, OLD DARLING!
EN GARDE!
C'MERE, YOU!

OH LUMMY!

SKKTAASHH!

SORRY, OLD MAN, BUT YOUR CONDITION APPEARS MOST GRAVE!

I ADVOCATE AMPUTATION! LIKE THUS —
— AND SO!

OH, FOR GOODNESS' SAKE! STAND STILL AND BURN, YOU BUGGER!
YOU KNOW, I DON'T THINK THESE FILTHY FLITCHES ARE ENTIRELY THE DULLARDS THEY APPEAR—

UHNN!
IT'S SO TIRESOME BEING RIGHT ALL THE TIME!

I DO SO HATE TO BE A BOTHER BUT IF SOMEONE COULD OBLIGE?

HHUUR?

ANYTHING ELSE?

NO, THANK YOU, DEAR FELLOW —
— I CAN MANAGE QUITE ADEQUATELY.

MWUUHH!

HGRRAGHH!
ZOMBIES — PTUH! SHIT ON 'EM!

PRESENT COMPANY EXCEPTED, BLACK BOB!
THAT'S ALL RIGHT! DON'T MIND ME!

NYUUHH!
OH NO Y'DON'T!

UHHH...

SHUT IT!

TIME YOU AN' ME 'AD WORDS, GIRLY!
I WOULDN'T COUNT ON IT, ASSWIPE!

UM... BOSS? PROBLEM!
MUHHHH...
Genuine Shoggoth
Alcohol

Genuine Shoggoth
Alcohol

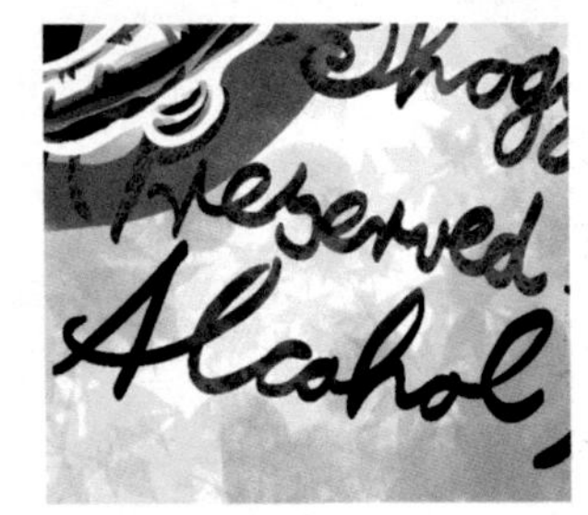
reserved
Alcohol

OH, FOR F—

KINVIG

KOFF! KOFF! GOOD LAD, BOB... GOOD LAD!
AT... AT LEAST THAT HARRIDAN HAS HAD HER JUST DESSERTS!

I'M AFRAID NOT. I TOOK A QUICK LOOK AROUND. THERE'S A BACK DOOR. SHE'S LONG GONE. THE CROWN TOO.

NOT SO FAST. THIS IS **MY** CITY — SHE AIN'T GONE 'TIL I SAYS SHE IS. 'SPECIALLY WHEN THIS FELLA ME LAD'S YET T'GIVE UP HIS SECRETS.
NNGGHH...

C'MON NOW! LET THE DOG SEE TH'RABBIT!

WHO SAYS DEAD MEN TELL NO TALES?

MORE POKE TO THE PUNT IF Y'PLEASE, BLACK BOB! WE AIN'T GOT ALL DAY!
IT'D HELP IF I KNEW WHERE WE WAS GOIN', BOSS...
I'LL MIND THE ROUTE, M'LAD, YOU MIND THE RIVER! THERE'S NASTIER THINGS'N TURDS AN' DEAD DOGS BOBBIN' ABOUT IN THIS MUCK!
I NEVER KNEW SUCH A PLACE EXISTED.
FEW DO. OLD MOTHER LONDON ALWAYS HAD MORE SONS THAN THE THAMES, BUT AS SHE GREW THE OLD GIRL NEEDED SHOULDER ROOM. SO ONE BY ONE, SHE BURIED HER CHILDREN ALIVE...

... THE FLEET, THE EFFRA, THE LONGBOURNE, WANDLE AND WALBROOK. SHE TRIED TO STIFLE 'EM ALL BUT THEY ENDURE DOWN HERE, FESTERIN' IN THE FILTH AN' THE DARK, WHERE ALL THE SECRETS OF THE CITY COME T'REST.

WHICH'S WHY WE'RE 'ERE. OUR PORT OF CALL —

— THE TEMPLE OF MITHRAS! THE NOTED REPOSITORY OF THE BROTHERHOOD OF THE BOOK!

STAY PUT AN' MIND THE BOAT.
THE BRAINBOX 'ERE AIN'T EXACTLY GONNA BE CHEERFUL AN' CHIPPER T'SEE ME, LET ALONE TURNIN' UP MOB HANDED.
LAST THING I NEED'S TRUFFLE 'IS FEATHERS!
HELLO? ANYONE 'OME?
WHAT RANK VILLAINY IS IT THAT BRINGS **YOU** DARKENING MY DOOR, FELON?
NOW THEN, IS THAT ANY WAY TO ADDRESS AN OLD FRIEND, ORLANDO?
I AM **DOCTOR** DOYLE TO YOU, CUR! OUR FRIENDSHIP AND AMITY IS LONG SPENT, SO DO NOT DARE DWELL ON SUCH PRESUMPTION!
YOU KNOW OUR CONTRACT. IF YOU HAVE BUSINESS HERE BE ABOUT IT OR ELSE BE GONE! YOUR PRESENCE SORELY TESTS MY PATIENCE AS IT IS!

HERE. THE TWENTY-EIGHTH PIECE OF THE JUDAS SILVER... IN EXCHANGE FOR INFORMATION.
AS AGREED, YOU HAVE BUT TWO MORE FAVOURS LEFT TO YOU AFTER THIS. THEN OUR CONTRACT IS FULFILLED. CROSS THIS THRESHOLD AFTER THAT, I SHALL ENSURE THE RUINATION OF YOU!
OH REALLY? AN' HOW'D Y'DO THAT, PRAY TELL?
I WILL TELL THE WORLD YOUR TRUE NAME.
NOW I ASSUME YOU HAVE COME ABOUT THE CROWN — THE JEWEL OF THE SEVEN STARS — ALTHOUGH THIS ITSELF IS A MISNOMER. THE JEWEL OF THE SEVEN STARS IS NOT THE CROWN BUT THE GEMSTONE SET UPON IT.
NOTHING ESCAPES YOU LOT, DOES IT? HISTORY'S CURTAIN TWITCHERS!
NECRONOMICON AL-HAZRED
SHOW SOME RESPECT, KNAVE! THE BROTHERHOOD OF THE BOOK WAS FOUNDED BY THE CUSTODIANS OF THE GREAT LIBRARY OF ALEXANDRIA AFTER IT WAS SACKED BY THE ROMANS! THEY VOWED NEVER AGAIN TO LET THE WISDOM OF MAN FALL PREY TO THE SWORD, THE TORCH AND THE BOOT HEEL!
IN THIS REFUGE, THE WRITINGS AND ARTIFACTS OF ANTIQUITY ARE KEPT SAFE AND THE SECRET HISTORY OF THE WORLD LAID DOWN FOR POSTERITY. I AM BUT ONE OF THAT FABLED ORDER TO HAVE STOOD WATCH HERE.
KNOWLEDGE IS POWER. IT IS ONLY BY KNOWING THE PAST THAT THE SECURITY OF THE FUTURE IS ENSURED.
AND THOUGH IT GALLS ME TO CARE FOR YOUR WELFARE, I MUST WARN YOU — THE GEM ITSELF IS SHROUDED IN DOOM!

'FOR A COUNTLESS AGE, THE JEWEL LAY UNTOUCHED AND REVERED IN ITS MOUNTAIN SHRINE, NORTH OF KHATMANDU...

'... UNTIL AN ARROGANT BRITISH ARMY OFFICER BY THE NAME OF **CAREW** CAME AND STOLE IT FOR HIS LADY LOVE.

'COME DAWN THEY FOUND HIM, SUNDERED AND SHREDDED. IT WAS BLAMED ON A ROGUE BEAST — A MAN-EATING TIGER. THOUGH NOT SPOKEN ALOUD, ALL KNEW THE FATE THAT BEFELL CAREW WAS OF NO NATURAL ORDER.

'OF THE JEWEL THERE WAS NO SIGN, ALTHOUGH ITS PASSAGE FROM EAST TO WEST CAN BE TRACKED BY THE TRAIL OF STRANGE DEATHS LEFT IN ITS WAKE.

'FOR A TIME, IT VANISHED FROM ALL PERCEPTION, ONLY TO REAPPEAR YEARS LATER MOUNTED INTO THE CROWN — A PRESENT FOR QUEEN VICTORIA.
'HOWEVER, IT WAS A **POISON PILL**, A GIFT OF CALAMITY THAT IT WAS HOPED WOULD BRING DEATH AND DESPAIR TO THE HEART OF THE EMPIRE.

'BUT THE QUEEN IS A WOMAN OF WIT AND GUILE. UNNERVED, SHE HAD IT PUT AWAY IN THE DEEPEST DUNGEON IN THE TOWER OF LONDON, WHERE, IT IS SAID, IN THE LONG WATCHES OF THE NIGHT, **UNNATURAL NOISES** COULD BE HEARD FROM WITHIN...'

SO WHY STEAL IT? WHO IN GOD'S NAME WOULD **WANT** SUCH A WOE?
THERE ARE SOME, BUT NOT IN **GOD**'S NAME! THE GEM ITSELF IS NOT CURSED, RATHER PLAGUED BY THE PRESENCE OF OTHERWORLDLY FORCES WHO DO NOT WISH ITS POTENTIAL RELEASED.

YOU'VE LOST ME.
THERE ARE THINGS IN THE VOID. OBSCENE, WRETCHED FORMS OF LIFE, PRESSING UPON THE SKIN OF THIS WORLD, ACHING FOR EGRESS.
SOME ARE SO VAST AS TO BE REALMS OF EXISTENCE IN THEMSELVES. OTHERS LURK BETWEEN LIFE AND DEATH, SEEKING TO PLUNDER AND PILLAGE. OTHERS STILL COME TO BEFOUL AND CORRUPT.

WE ARE SAFE SO LONG AS THERE ARE **GATEKEEPERS**, PROTECTORS WHO COME WHEN SUMMONED. BEASTS OF FIRE AND SCALES AND WINGS...
DRAGONS... YOU'RE TALKING ABOUT **DRAGONS**!

THE JEWEL IS A DRAGON'S EGG — A MALE — A PROGENITOR. THE **LAST** OF ITS KIND. IF IT IS DESTROYED, SO FALLS OUR DEFENCE. WHOEVER HAS THE JEWEL HAS THE MEANS TO NEGATE THE EVIL SURROUNDING IT...
Ova Draconis Placent Aut Elixa Aut Fricta

... OR IS IN LEAGUE WITH IT?
I DUG THIS OUT ONE O'THEIR LACKEYS. ZOMBIE, REAL NASTY 'UN.

ALPHA AND OMEGA — THE BEGINNING AND THE END. THIS IS FROM A **RESURRECTION GUN**, THE SOUL OF ITS VICTIM SLAVED TO THE BULLET THAT KILLED THEM.
THESE PEOPLE ARE NOT AMATEURS. THEY HAVE POWER AND THE SKILL TO USE IT. I HAVE BUT ONE WORD OF ADVICE FOR YOU...

... **PRAY**!

THERE SHE GOES! THE ROOTINEST, TOOTINEST, SHARP-SHOOTIN' LIL' LADY WEST OF THE PECOS!
BUFFALO BILL'S WILD WEST AND CONGRESS OF ROUGH RIDERS OF THE WORLD.
FINAL PERFORMANCE
BUFFALO BILL CODY'S AUTHENTIC WILD WEST CIRCUS
LET'S HEAR IT F'MISS ANNIE OAKLEY, FOLKS!
BUFFALO BILL CODY'S AUTHENTIC WILD WEST CIRCUS
YEEE-HAAA!
MUCH OBLIGED, Y'ALL!
OOOOOH!
CLAPCLAPCLAPCL
AN' LET'S NOT FORGET THE REST O'THE GANG!
SILENT ROBERT — THE HUMAN BULLS-EYE!
CHIEF HORSE FEATHERS AND HIS NOBLE BRAVES!
EGG SHEN, MYSTIC OF THE ORIENT, AND WHISTLIN' DIXIE AND HER CALCULATIN' PALAMINOS!
AND FINALLY, I, WILLIAM F. CODY, YOUR HUMBLE, HONOURED HOST, BID YOU ALL A FOND FAREWELL.
FOR THOUGH WE MAY TRAVEL AN' TRAVAIL FAR AND WIDE, WE WILL ALL SURELY CARRY WITH US SOME O'THE WARMTH AN' GENEROSITY WE'VE MET HERE WITH YOU FINE FOLKS.

SO, AH BID GOOD NIGHT TO Y'ALL... AN' TO ALL, GOOD NIGHT!
BRAVO!
GOOD SHOW!
HURRAH!
CLAP CLAP CLAP
THE ROUSTABOUTS STARTED CRATIN' UP YET, COOKIE?
YES, SIR.
GOOD. CAN'T WAIT T'SHAKE THE SHIT FROM THIS 'BURG OFFA M'BOOT HEEL. WHAT Y'DOIN' BACK HERE, ANYWAYS?
UH, WE GOT **COMPANY**. SAYS HE'S RUN AWAY T'JOIN THE CIRCUS.
THAT SO? I RECKON Y'**FOLKS** MIGHT HAVE SOMETHIN' T'SAY 'BOUT THAT, MISTER... ?
MOYES, SIR. **DAVID MOYES**. AND MY PARENTS DON'T KNOW I'M HERE. I SNEAKED OUT WHILE THEY WERE ASLEEP! I'VE READ ALL ABOUT YOUR ADVENTURES IN MY **COMIC CUTS**! ALL WIZARD WHEEZES AND JOLLY JAPES!

JOLLY JAPES, SURE. WE'RE JUS' JAPIN' ALL THE TIME!
TELL Y'WHAT, YOU GO WITH SHOCKEYE HERE, AN' WE'LL TALK 'BOUT IT LATER OVER A BITE TO EAT. WHAT D'YOU SAY?
RATHER!

I'LL HAVE HIM GRILLED AN' SMOTHERED IN ONIONS.
YES, BOSS.

S'MATTER, SHEN? Y'LOOK LIKE Y'LOST A NICKEL AN' FOUND A TURD IN Y'POCKET.
THIS IS FOOLISHNESS! WE SHOULD NOT HAVE STAYED! WE SHOULD HAVE LEFT ONCE THE CROWN WAS RECOVERED!
WHAT, AN' DISAPPOINT ALL THESE FINE FOLK? AIN'T Y'EVER HEARD THE SAYIN' THAT 'THE SHOW MUST GO ON'?
YOU DID SO BECAUSE IT APPEALED TO YOUR MONSTROUS EGO! TO RISK ALL AND DANCE UPON THE RAZOR'S EDGE!
THE BRITISH GOVERNMENT HAS MORE THAN AN INKLING OF WHO WE ARE, I'M CERTAIN! THAT THEY SET THEIR GROTESQUE AND HIS MENAGERIE UPON US IS PROOF OF IT!
YEAH, WELL, LIL' MISS ANNIE COOKED THEIR GOOSE.
ARE YOU CERTAIN? EVEN SO, MORE WILL COME! WE ARE RISKING ALL FOR YOUR ARROGANCE!
DON'T TELL ME M'JOB, OLD MAN! I KNOW EXACTLY WHAT'S AT STAKE HERE!
OR HAVE Y'FORGOTTEN WHO Y'WORK FOR?
NO... NO! I APOLOGISE! I MEANT NO DISRESPECT!
'COURSE NOT. NOW WHY DON'T Y'BE A GOOD BOY AN' GO PACK UP Y'SILK JIM-JAMS AN' ALL Y'WEIRD JUNK. 'CAUSE COME MORNIN' WE'LL BE LONG GONE...

'... AN' NO ONE WILL BE ANY THE WISER!'
WHAT'S THE PLAN, BOSS?
THE PLAN, ROBERT, IS YOU DO WHATEVER I SAY 'TIL EITHER THE JOB'S DONE OR Y'DROP DOWN DEAD... AGAIN.
RIGHTY-HO!
HYDE PARK

HOWEVER, MISS SCARLET, I'VE ANOTHER TASK FOR YOU.
BUT I'M NOT AFRAID. I CAN FIGHT! I CAN HOLD MY OWN!

HEH HEH HEH! RUBADUB! RUBADUB!
OH, LANGUAGE! YOU CAN BE SO CRUDE AT TIMES!

I WANT YOU TO RUN AN ERRAND FOR ME. TAKE THIS MISSIVE TO LIMEHOUSE. DELIVER IT PERSONALLY INTO THE HANDS OF THE EMPRESS.
THE... EMPRESS?

IS THERE A PROBLEM?
N-NO... IT... IT'S JUST THE STORIES... ABOUT THE UNNATURAL THINGS SHE'S HAD DONE TO PEOPLE...
THEN YOU MUST BE SURE TO BE ON YOUR BEST BEHAVIOUR. NOW OFF YOU TROT, THERE'S A DEAR.

EXCUSE ME, OLD DARLING, BUT WASN'T THAT A LITTLE HARSH? GIRL'S TERRIFIED!
FIERY JACK, YOUVE BEEN IN MY EMPLOY LONGEST OF ALL, SO I VALUE YOUR OPINION MOST HIGHLY. ABOVE THAT OF MY MORNIN' BOWEL MOVEMENT IN FACT, AN' JUST AS WORTHY!
ANYONE ELSE FANCY CHIPPIN' IN THEIR TWO-PEN'ORTH?
RIGHT THEN, LET'S AMBLE —

'— FOR NOW THERE WILL BE VIOLENCE!'

BHUU-RRPP!
UGH. KID WAS STRINGIER THAN HE LOOKED.
HEY, SHOCKEYE, WHAT'S FER DESSERT? Y'GOT ANY MORE O'THAT BLOOD CUSTARD AN' THEM SWEET PICKLED TWINS LEFT?

HEY THERE, COOKIE! GIT Y'SOUSED ASS IN HERE!

WHAT THE... ?

SORRY, CHUM. HE'S INDISPOSED.
SO 'ARD T'GET GOOD STAFF THESE DAYS, AIN'T IT?

WELL, WELL, WELL! WHAT D'WE HAVE HERE?
LOOKS LIKE THE CIRCUS HAS COME T'TOWN! SORRY, FELLAS, THIS PITCH IS ALL DONE AND PLAYED OUT!
SHUT Y'YAP, YANK! I AIN'T HERE T'PRANCE AN' PARLAY! YOU KNOW WHAT WE'VE COME FOR! HAND IT OVER IF Y'KNOW WHAT'S GOOD FOR YEH!
THE JEWEL O'THE SEVEN STARS?
A DRAGON'S EGG!

HEH, Y'DONE Y'HOMEWORK, I'LL GRANT YEH. SO Y'KNOW I AIN'T GONNA JUS' GIVE IT UP 'CAUSE Y'ASKIN'!

FEH! I DON'T GIVE A MONKEY'S RUBY-RED ARSE WHAT YOU DO! I AIN'T ARSKIN! I'M TELLIN'!
AN' I AIN'T GIVIN'! YOU COME IN HERE YAPPIN' AT ME LIKE A LIL' JUNKYARD DOG — YOU KNOW WHO I AM, CROOKED MAN?

I KNOW WHO YOU AIN'T... AN' YOU AIN'T CODY! I KNOW CODY FROM WAY BACK, AN' HE KNOWS ME. YOU AIN'T 'IM!

WELL, NOW. THAT PUTS A WHOLE NEW SHINE ON THE OCCASION, DON'T IT?

IT DON'T CHANGE NOTHIN'!

NHH!

NNH-NUHH-NNNH!

GOOD LAD, TONGA! THERE'LL BE ANOTHER KITTEN FOR Y'TEA TONIGHT.
HOTCHA!

RIGHT THEN, YOU LOT. TEAR THIS BLEEDIN' MONKEY HOUSE APART AN' FIND ME THAT FRIGGIN' STONE!
ANYONE GIVES YOU ANY BOTHER, DO FOR 'EM. THEY AIN'T CIVVIES, THEY KNOWS THE GAME.
I DON'T THINK THAT'S GOING TO BE MUCH OF A PROBLEM, SIR...

BUFFALO-BILL CODY'S
AUTHENTIC
WILD WEST CIRCUS
... LOOKS LIKE THE BLESSED BEGGARS HAVE DOWNED TOOLS!
I SAY! THESE MEN ARE DEAD — SNIFF — AND RIPE!
EXCEPT... I COULD HAVE SWORN THEY LOOKED LIKE NOR-MAL CHAPS WHEN WE ARRIVED...
HUH! THESE BLOKES AREN'T EVEN HUMAN —
— THEY'RE SOLID WOOD! HOW'S THAT, THEN?
WOK WOK
MAGIC, THAT'S HOW! PTUH — SHIT ON IT!
THEY'RE LIKE THE CORPSES BACK AT KINVIG'S. MARIONETTES MADE FROM DEAD MEN AN' BITTER OAK AN' DRESSED IN A GLAMOUR TO LOOK NORMAL! 'CEPT NOW CODY'S CROAKED THEIR STRINGS 'AVE BEEN SNIPPED!
ALSO MEANS THERE AIN'T NO ONE 'ROUND T'GIVE US GRIEF, SO HOP TO IT!

YUK!
HRRRRR! HUGGA-MUGGA!
YOU'RE DISGUSTING!

HEH! S'ABOUT RIGHT!

ANY-THIN'?
NOT AS SUCH, BUT THERE'S SOMETHING THAT YOU SHOULD SEE...
...OR RATHER **SOME-ONE**!

A FAT BLOKE? Y'FOUND ME A **FAT BLOKE**?
HE'S NOT LIKE THE REST. HE'S ALIVE AND BREATHING BUT IT SEEMS HIS MIND'S GONE.

WHAT'S THIS? FOOT-PRINTS...?
HALF A DOZEN AT LEAST BUT ONLY GOING THE ONE WAY, NONE COMING BACK. IT'S A MYSTERY.

THEN WE'LL JUST 'AVE T'MAKE FAT BOY 'ERE FIND HIS VOICE THEN, WON'T WE?

Y'CAN TRY BUT AH WOULDN'T HOLD Y'BREATH WAITIN'.
Y'SEE ROBERT AIN'T EXACTLY BUILT F'CONVERSATION.
GAH! I SHOULDA KNOWN Y'WENT DOWN TOO EASY!
GUUUAHHHH!
OH DEAR GOD!
HE'S MORE WHAT YOU'D CALL A HOME FROM HOME F'SOME OF US!
YOU'RE IN SOME PRETTY SHIT NOW, BOYS!

C'MON THEN, COWBOY, LET'S HAVE SOME! THAT'S IF Y'GOT THE PLUMS FOR IT!
TEAR 'EM UP, BOYS! DON'T LEAVE NOTHIN' BUT SHIT STAINS AN' CHUNKY SOUP!
NYYAARGH!
YEAH? AN' ARSE'OLES T'YOU AN' ALL, UGLY!
BDAM!
HOTCHA! GHRROWRR!
OI, LADIES MAN! TUCK IT DOWN Y'LEG! YOU'RE ON THE CLOCK, REMEMBER?
SHONUFF!

OOH, BAD BABY! NEEDS A SPANK!
GIT ALONG, LIL' DOGGY!
UGLK!
BADOOM!
MUTU!
YOU'RE WELCOME!
FRYING TONIGHT!
YOU ARE A TROUBLED SOUL, BUT I KNOW WHAT IT IS YOU CRAVE. I KNOW YOUR HEART'S DESIRE.
THAT SO, OLD DARLING?

INDEED! SEE FOR YOURSELF!
GYAAHHH!

OH GOD... DEAR GOD! MY HANDS...

MY FACE! DEAR GOD IN HEAVEN, I CAN FEEL MY **FACE**!

JOHN, I'M **NORMAL**! I'M **HUMAN** AGAIN!
JACK, IT'S A **TRICK**! HOLD ON, I'M COMING!

WHAT THE DEVIL— ?

DIE, DAMN YOUR HEINOUS HEATHEN HIDE!

HNUH... I SAY, THESE DAMN THINGS ARE HEAVY!

AH, HELLO THERE! SORRY TO BARGE IN UNANNOUNCED BUT THE ELEMENT OF SURPRISE AND ALL THAT.
NOW, IF YOU'LL ALL JUST BEHAVE YOURSELVES, WE'LL HAVE THIS OVER WITH IN A JIFFY.

ASHENDEN, YOU KNOB! WHAT'RE **YOU** DOIN' HERE? WE'RE—
OH... OH, I GET IT! WE'VE BEEN PLAYED, AIN'T WE? WE'VE BEEN HAD!

YOU SOUND SURPRISED. IT'S WHAT WE DO — WE **LIE**. WE'RE SPIES! WE'RE VERY GOOD AT IT TOO.
DID YOU REALLY IMAGINE HER MAJESTY'S GOVERNMENT WOULD ENTRUST SUCH A VITAL TASK TO A SCROFULOUS LITTLE TICK LIKE YOU AND THIS MENAGERIE?
AN' THAT SHOW AT YOUR OFFICE?

A SMALL CHARADE. A SHADOW-PLAY.
IT WAS THE PROFESSOR'S IDEA. TURNED OUT QUITE THE CAPITAL SCHEME. YOU DO ALL THE FOOT SLOG AND DIRTY WORK, BEAT THE LONG GRASS TO DRIVE OUT THE TIGERS, AND WE COLLECT THE SPOILS BEFORE YOU FIND SOME WAY TO PULL THE RUG FROM UNDER US.

THIS REALLY AIN'T YOUR DAY, IS IT?
TELL ME ABOUT IT!

NOW, I'D LOVE TO STAY AND CHITCHAT BUT I'M SURE WE'VE ALL PLACES TO BE. SO, I SHALL ASK THIS ONLY ONCE — THE STONE. KINDLY HAND IT OVER.
AIN'T GONNA HAPPEN, PENCIL-NECK!

OH, HOW TIRESOME.
VERY WELL. KILL THEM ALL. WE'LL FIND THE INFERNAL THING OURSELVES AFTERWARDS.

BUDDA BUDDA BUDDA BUDDA
GOOD GOIN', BOB. GET THE GANG TOGETHER, WE'RE GOIN' INSIDE THE FAT BLOKE. S'GOTTA BE WHERE THEY'RE KEEPIN' THE GEEGAW.
RIGHTY-HO, GUV!

BUDDA
BUDDA
BUDDA
BUDDA
SPAK
OH NO Y'DON'T, Y'SPINEY-BACKED LIL' SHITKICKER! I SEE YOU!
ANNIE! GIT BACK INSIDE ROBERT! DON'T LET THEM SONS OF BITCHES NEAR THE JEWEL!

NFF! DANG, THIS WAS M'BEST SUIT—

NOW AH'M GONNA HAVE T'**CHANGE**!

C'MON, JACK! GET THE LEAD OUT AN' STRIKE A LIGHT! I CAN'T SEE A HAND IN FRONT OF ME FACE!

THIS AIN'T RIGHT! I WAS FINE — FLESH AND BLOOD AGAIN! IT'S NOT FAIR!
IT AIN'T RIGHT!

I'LL TELL Y'WHAT AIN'T RIGHT, LADDO! 'AVIN' THE WOOL PULLED OVER ME EYES BY A CHINLESS WONDER, F'STARTERS! THEN THERE'S THE LITTLE MATTER OF US RUNNIN' AROUND IN THE DARK, OUT-NUMBERED AN' ARSE-DEEP IN GRIEF WHILE YOU BOO-HOO OVER Y'LOST LOOKS!

WE GO BACK AWAYS, JACKY, SO I'M GIVIN' Y'ONE CHANCE —
— GET Y'SELF SORTED AN' YOUR HEAD LIT OR I'LL POP A PLUG IN Y'TURNIP! WE SINGIN' FROM THE SAME HYMN SHEET?

YES... YES, WE ARE.

THERE.

OH DEAR GOD IN HEAVEN!
UGH! T-THEY'RE NOT DEAD! THEY'VE ALL BEEN STACKED LIKE LOGS, LIKE BRICKS, BUT THEY'RE NOT DEAD!

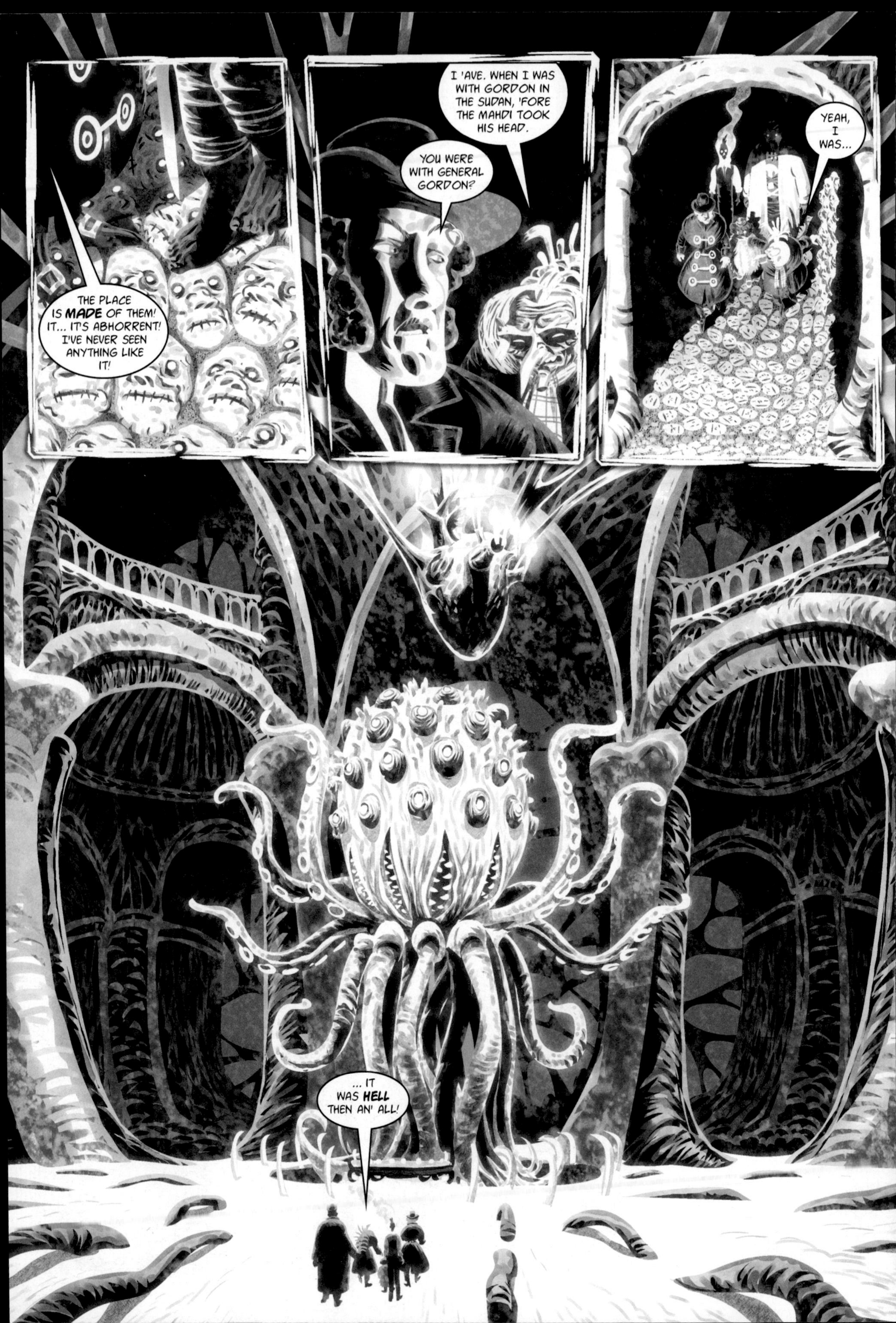
THE PLACE IS MADE OF THEM! IT... IT'S ABHORRENT! I'VE NEVER SEEN ANYTHING LIKE IT!
YOU WERE WITH GENERAL GORDON?
I 'AVE. WHEN I WAS WITH GORDON IN THE SUDAN, 'FORE THE MAHDI TOOK HIS HEAD.
YEAH, I WAS...
... IT WAS HELL THEN AN' ALL!

HE'S SCARED, BOSS. CAN'T SAY I BLAME HIM. I THOUGHT I WAS LONG PAST POPPIN' A LOG IN ME DRAWERS BUT I'VE GOT A SERIOUS CASE OF THE WILLIES, I CAN TELL YOU!
GREAT STEAMIN' ARSE'OLES! WHEN DID YOU ALL TURN INTO A BUNCH O'JESSIES?
TONGA, GET Y'SELF UP THERE, BOY! FETCH ME THAT GEM — THE SHINY ONE, MIND!
NUN-UH!
THIS AIN'T A CHURCH SOCIAL, Y'LITTLE FART-CATCHER! NOW HOP TO!
FUGU!
UP Y'GO! DON'T WORRY, YOU'LL BE DONE IN TWO SHAKES OF A LAMB'S TAIL.
BOO-HOO L'AMOUR?
OF COURSE I DO. NOW OFF YOU POP!
UH, FORGIVE ME FOR PRESSING THE POINT, BUT WHAT HAPPENED BEFORE? YOU SAID YOU'D ALREADY SEEN SOMETHING LIKE THIS...
OH YEAH...
BACK THEN, SOME O'THE MAHDI'S MOB HAD GOT 'OLD OF AN ANCIENT MAGIC BOOK BY SOME MAD ARAB AN' WAS RAISIN' HAVOC, CALLIN' UP DJINN AN' WOTNOT...

'I WAS IN A CAIRO NICK, WAITIN' ON A LONG DROP AN' A SHORT STOP FOR M'TROUBLES, WHEN GENERAL GORDON HIMSELF TURNED UP, OFFERIN' T'PARDON ME, WITH A PROVISO.
'HE'D HEARD OF MY CRIMINAL INCLINATIONS AND PARTNERED ME UP WITH A MATE OF 'IS, AN OLD SOLDIER NAME O'DICK SHARPE. WE WAS T'SNEAK BEHIND ENEMY LINES AN' NICK THE BOOK.
''COURSE, I AGREED. ANYTHIN' T'GET OUT OF THAT HOLE. BESIDES, LIFTIN' A BOOK, HOW HARD COULD IT BE?
'NEEDLESS T'SAY, IT ALL WENT TITS UP.
'I WOULD'VE COPPED IT FOR SURE IF IT WASN'T FOR DICKY SHARPE —
'— HE WAS THE BRAVEST MAN I'D EVER MET.'

BINGO!
DOWN YOU COME, NOW. I'VE GOT YOU.

GOOD LAD. RIGHT THEN, KIDDIES, HOME TME...

BDAM!
GHTT!

YEE-HAAAH!
BDAM!
BDAM!

SIR!
BDAM!

HAH! NOW **THAT**, MY FRIENDS, IS GODDAMN **PAYBACK**!

NAH, LOVE —
— THIS IS!
BLAM
AHH! SONOVABITCH!
HA HA HA! OW!
WAS THAT IT? THAT Y'BEST SHOT?
I ONLY NEEDED THE ONE. YOU SHOULD RECOGNISE IT —
WHAT THE... ?
— IT'S Y'RESURRECTION BULLET. I HAD IT REFILLED.
GIIIIAAAAAHHH!
MMWWUUH!
HGGRRR...

BLAM
NOW THAT, MY DEAR —
— IS PAYBACK!
BOSS, YOU OKAY?
JUST PEACHY. CORK AN' HORSEHAIR WAISTCOAT — STOPS BULLETS A TREAT!
TA.
RIGHT THEN, TIME T'BE NIMBLE AND SPRY, GENTS. IF ASHENDEN AND CODY ARE STILL AT EACH OTHERS' THROATS, WE CAN SLIP AWAY WITH NEITHER OF 'EM BEIN' NONE THE WISER.
JACK, WAIT. YOU'VE KNOWN THE BOSS LONGEST. YOU EVER NOTICED ANYTHING... UNUSUAL ABOUT HIM?
THAT'S AN UNDERSTATEMENT. THAT DEVIL'S A MYSTERY WRAPPED IN AN ENIGMA. WHY?
WHEN I CAUGHT HIM, I FELT SOMETHING... NOT A PADDED VEST, MORE LIKE... A HARNESS STRAPPED TO HIM.
I DON'T THINK HIS BACK, HIS DEFORMITY, IS REAL. I THINK IT'S SOME KIND OF COSTUME...
WHICH RAISES THE QUESTION...
... WHO IN GOD'S NAME IS HE?

IT'S GONE QUIET...
AIN'T IT JUST!
SHIT T'SIXPENCE IT AIN'T GOOD NEWS FOR US!
AH.
FUGU MOI!
SIR TRISTRAM
BUGGER!

PLEASE... DEAR GOD! FOR PITY'S SAKE, HELP ME!

WELL, LOOKEE HERE ! IF YOU AIN'T A BUNCH O'BAD PENNIES! GUESS THE JOKE'S ON ME F'SENDIN' A WOMAN T'DO A MAN'S JOB!
HOLD ON A SECOND, WILL YEH? I'M JUST FINISHIN' UP HERE.
OH, PLEASE GOD... DO SOMETHING!

HUSH UP NOW AN' TAKE IT LIKE A MAN!
NHU! GHU! GIIIAAAAA—

HELL, YOU BRITS ARE STRINGY BASTARDS!
OKAY, HERE'S HOW IT'S GONNA BE! NO MORE GAMES! GIMME THE GODDAMN JEWEL AN I'LL END Y'ALL REAL QUICK AND PAINLESS. KEEP SCREWIN' ME AROUND, AN' I'LL SHOW YOU A WORLD O'HURT THAT'LL MAKE WHAT I DID T'BONEY BOY THERE SEEM LIKE A NIGHT IN A TEXAS CATHOUSE!
THAT CLEAR ENOUGH FOR Y'ALL?

CHRIST ON A STICK! WHAT KIND OF HORRORSHOW ARE YOU?
I AIN'T NO MONSTER, LITTLE MAN! I'M AMONGST THE BLESSED! I'M THE PROPHET OF THE LORDS O'THE NEW CHURCH. I'M HERE T'PREPARE THE WAY F'THEIR RETURN, T'SEE THAT ALL THAT WAS LAID LOW IS RAISED HIGH AGAIN.
I WAS ALSO A MAN ONCE — VILE, CALLOW AN' VULGAR LIKE YOU. ALL I CARED ABOUT WAS HARD LIQUOR, COLD CASH AND HOT WOMEN...
'... I PREYED ON THE GULLIBLE AN' INNOCENT, LEADIN' WAGON TRAINS OUT WEST 'FORE BUSHWACKIN' 'EM, TAKIN' THEIR GOLD, SELLIN' THEIR WOMEN AN' HORSES AN' SLAUGHTERIN' THE REST.
' 'CEPT LAST TIME OUT WE GOT SNOWED IN UP IN THE SIERRA NEVADAS. WE LIT INTO A CAVE T'WAIT IT OUT. WISHFUL THINKIN' — IT WAS THREE MONTHS O'WHITE HELL.

'FINALLY I LIT ON A GREAT LAKE, SO FAR AN' WIDE Y'COULDN'T SEE ITS EDGE. ITS SURFACE WAS AS SMOOTH AS BLACK GLASS. I KNEW, SOMEHOW, IT WAS A **HOLY PLACE**.

'I SUNK TO M'KNEES AN' PRAYED TO ANY SORTA GOD WHO'D BE LISTENIN' TO COME BREAK ME OF M'BURDEN. I'D GIVE M'LIFE, M'HEART... M'**SOUL**!

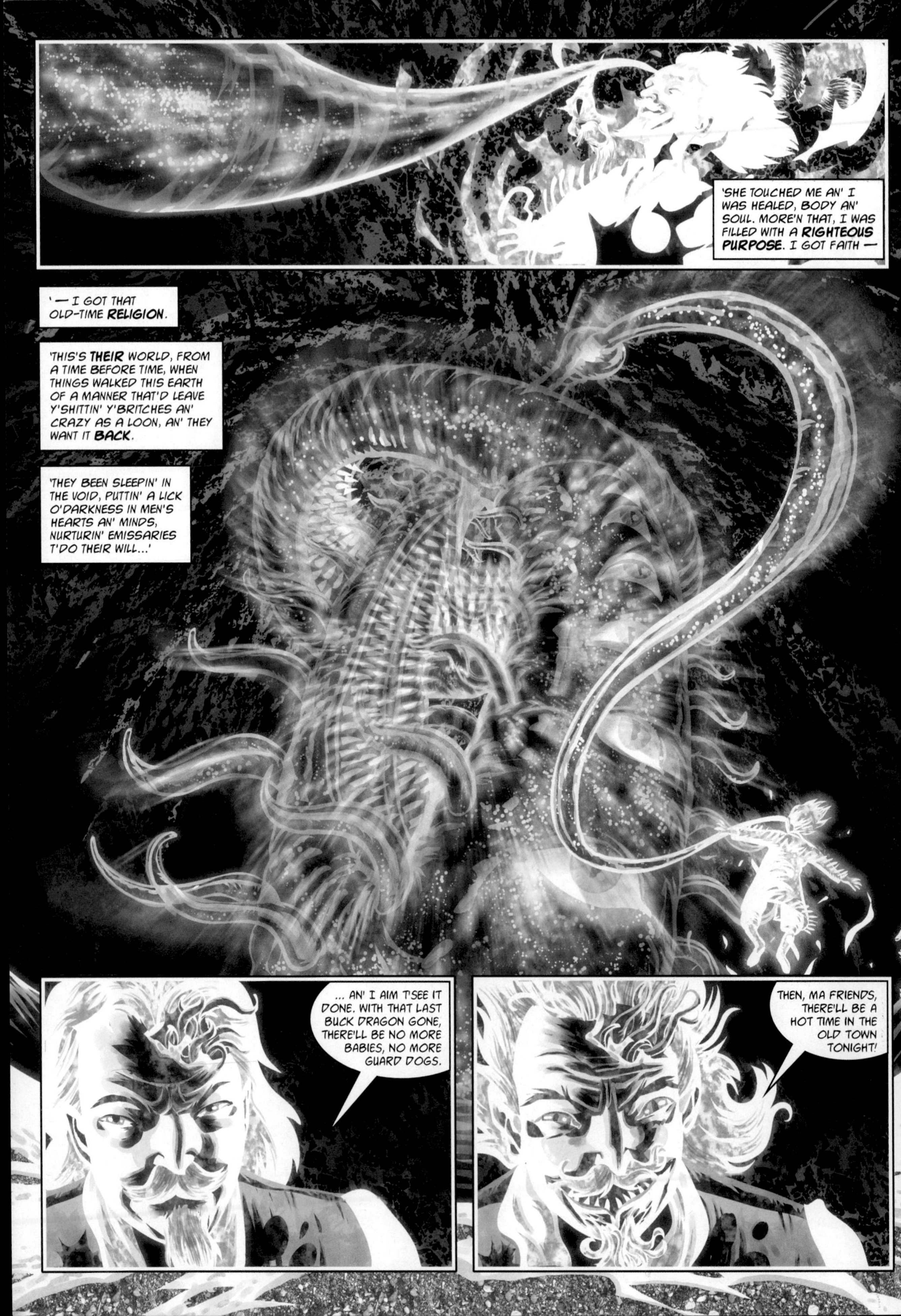

'SHE TOUCHED ME AN' I WAS HEALED, BODY AN' SOUL. MORE'N THAT, I WAS FILLED WITH A RIGHTEOUS PURPOSE. I GOT FAITH —
'— I GOT THAT OLD-TIME RELIGION.
'THIS'S THEIR WORLD, FROM A TIME BEFORE TIME, WHEN THINGS WALKED THIS EARTH OF A MANNER THAT'D LEAVE Y'SHITTIN' Y'BRITCHES AN' CRAZY AS A LOON, AN' THEY WANT IT BACK.
'THEY BEEN SLEEPIN' IN THE VOID, PUTTIN' A LICK O'DARKNESS IN MEN'S HEARTS AN' MINDS, NURTURIN' EMISSARIES T'DO THEIR WILL...'
... AN' I AIM T'SEE IT DONE. WITH THAT LAST BUCK DRAGON GONE, THERE'LL BE NO MORE BABIES, NO MORE GUARD DOGS.
THEN, MA FRIENDS, THERE'LL BE A HOT TIME IN THE OLD TOWN TONIGHT!

ENOUGH JAWIN'! TIME'S UP, TIME T'DIE!
GOTTA CONFESS, I'VE BEEN LOOKIN' FORWARD T'THIS!
HUKKH!

OI!
NFF!

LEAVE 'IM ALONE!
GHK!

DAMN, DEAD MAN! Y'GOT GRIT — I LIKE THAT! I COULD USE A FIGHTIN' FLITCH LIKE YOU!
UHH! GET STUFFED!
SURE, YOU'LL FIT IN JUS' FINE ONCE SHEN GETS Y'HEAD THINKIN' MY WAY. IN THE MEANTIME —

— WHY DON'T Y'SIT THIS ONE OUT?
BEBE FUGU MORTE!

NOW, WHERE WERE WE?
Y'TOO LATE, CHUM! Y'BUGGERED!

YOU WANT THIS?

TAKE IT! FOR THE GOOD IT'LL DO YEH!

WHAT THE... ?

WHERE'D THE HELL IT GO? WHAT DID Y'DO TO IT?
AN' WHAT THE GOOD GODDAMN IS THIS STUFF!

LOTUS PETALS, THE COLOUR OF DEATH. SHE LIKES TO MAKE AN ENTRANCE...

LOTUS PETALS? THE WHITE LOTUS EMPRESS? BUT... IT CAN'T BE HER... SHE'S DEA—
SHHIFF!

SHHUFF!

NO! NO! THIS AIN'T RIGHT!
THE FUN'S JUST STARTIN', TRUST ME! YOU AIN'T SEEN NOTHIN' YET!

HGRRRR! KNEEL, CUR!
HKKSSSS! AND PRAY FOR A SWIFT DEATH!

FOR SHE COMES!

THE EMPRESS COMES!

ゴジラ
ゴジラ
ゴジラ
ゴジラ

WHAT, AM I SUPPOSED T'BE **IMPRESSED**?

HOW THE HELL...?

AH, OKAY. THAT'LL DO IT.

HEH! Y'GOT TH'WINNIN' HAND FER NOW, SO DO WHAT Y'GOTTA, Y'SLANT-EYED BITCH. BUT MARK ME WELL, YOU AIN'T GOT WHAT IT TAKES TO **STOP** WHAT'S COMIN'!
THIS AIN'T OVER!

IT IS FOR YOU.

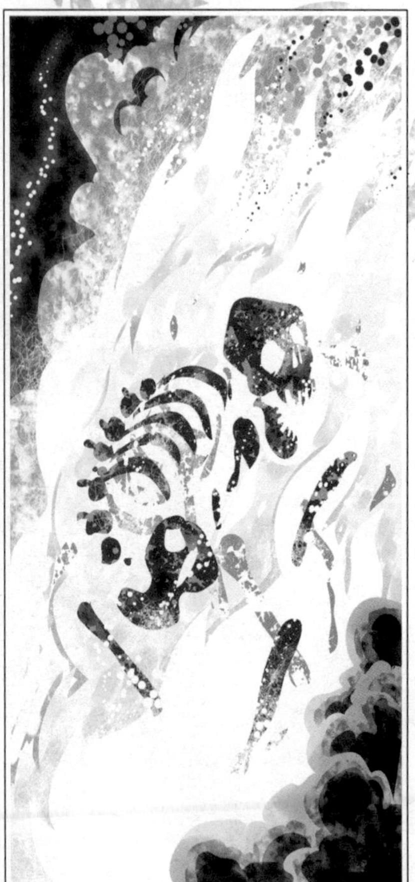

BOW YOUR HEADS!

EMPRESS. A JOY AS EVER.
I DO NOT LEAVE LIMEHOUSE LIGHTLY. THERE ARE FEW WHOSE SUMMONS I WOULD HEED, YET HERE I AM, WHICH PLACES YOU IN MY DEBT — A POSITION MANY WOULD GO OUT OF THEIR WAY TO AVOID.
BUT THEN, YOU ALWAYS DID LIKE TO LIVE DANGEROUSLY.
I-I KNEW I WAS GETTIN' OUT OF MY DEPTH. YOU WERE THE ONLY ONE WHO KNEW 'BOUT THIS STUFF. THAT CODY, HE WOULD'VE QUEERED THE PITCH FOR ALL OF US...
HIS MASTERS MAY STILL YET... BUT NOT TODAY.
FORTUNATELY, THIS ITEM BALANCES THE SCALES IN LIEU OF YOUR DEBT. MY PET HAS BEEN BROODY OF LATE AND REQUIRES A MATE. EVERY WOMAN SHOULD HAVE A CHILD.
SPEAKING OF WHICH... HOW IS THE BOY?
OUR SON IS WELL. YOU WILL SEE HIM ON THE APPOINTED DAY EACH YEAR, AS PER OUR AGREEMENT. UNTIL THEN, OUR BUSINESS HERE IS CONCLUDED.
THE SIGHT OF THIS DOGS' DINNER WILL TURN A FEW HAIRS COME MORNIN'!
NO, IT WILL NOT. AS YOU WELL KNOW, THE ONE THING I MOST DESPISE ABOVE ALL —

'— IS LOOSE ENDS.'
TITBITS
WILD WEST INFERNO
CASUALTIES HIGH AT COWBOY CIRCUS CATASTROPHE
UK CODY A FRAUD! REAL BUFFALO BILL SPEAKS OUT!
THERE YOU GO, BOB! RIGHT AS NINEPENCE!
THANK YOU, MISS SCARLET. I'M MOST OBLIGED.
YOWSA BOCOUP! HOO-HAA!
PERSONALLY, I'M ASTONISHED WE'RE HERE TO SEE ANOTHER DAY. I'VE BEEN IN SOME GRIM SCRAPES BUT I WAS CERTAIN WE'D NOT LEAVE THAT INFERNAL PLACE UPRIGHT AND BREATHING.
IT WAS ALMOST ENOUGH TO DRIVE ONE ONTO THE STRAIGHT AND NARROW.
EVEN SO, I DON'T THINK I'VE EVER SEEN HIM IN SUCH A FUG. I'LL WARRANT IT'S TO DO WITH THE EMPRESS. SHE'S NOT TO BE CROSSED LIGHTLY.
THOUGH WE'LL PAY THE PRICE IF HE DOES! WE'VE LONG ALLIED OUR FORTUNES WITH HIS, YET WHAT HAPPENS WHEN HIS TURN? WE DON'T EVEN KNOW WHO HE TRULY IS...
IT'S TIME WE LOOKED TO OURSELVES AND OUR OWN FUTURE.
'CAESAR NEEDS HIS EMPIRE... BUT DOES THE EMPIRE NEED CAESAR?'

D'ISRAELI SKETCHBOOK & COVERS GALLERY

2000 AD Prog 1525: Cover by **D'Israeli**

2000 AD Prog 1575: Cover by **D'Israe**

▲ Ian Edginton's sketch showing the malformations on Stickleback's spine.

▼▲ My first concept sketch; here Stickleback is much younger and more Tim Burtonesque. Ian had a very clear idea how Stickleback's spine was to look, so I went through several versions of the spine until Ian finally did me a sketch to show how he saw it.

◄ The Stickleback concept sketch presented to Matt Smith in the series pitch to *2000 AD*.

► A variation of the same drawing, done in the Stickleback "paint and collage" technique. This was used to accompany an interview in the *Megazine*.

▼ The first versions of Black Bob looked much more aggressive than the final 'genial zombie'. Tonga has remained more or less unchanged from the first sketch.

► The thinner, aggressive version of Bob.

▼ Fiery jack was more or less there first time.

31-03-04

STICKLEBACK
– FIERY JACK

WHEN THE ARMS ARE BURNT, THE TENDONS CONTRACT AND THE ARMS CURL UP. WHILE JACK CAN USE HIS ARMS NORMALLY, THEY COME TO REST IN THIS POSITION

SHOULD HIS CLOTHING ALSO BE CHARRED?

An early idea was for Stickleback to have a Sherlock Holmes-style adversary who was actually just as evil and conniving as Stickleback was. This sinister fellow eventually became the more sympathetic Scotland Yard detective Valentine Bey.

▲ The first try at Mister Peepers and Mister Lug. I couldn't make the character work until Ian suggested they wear top hats.

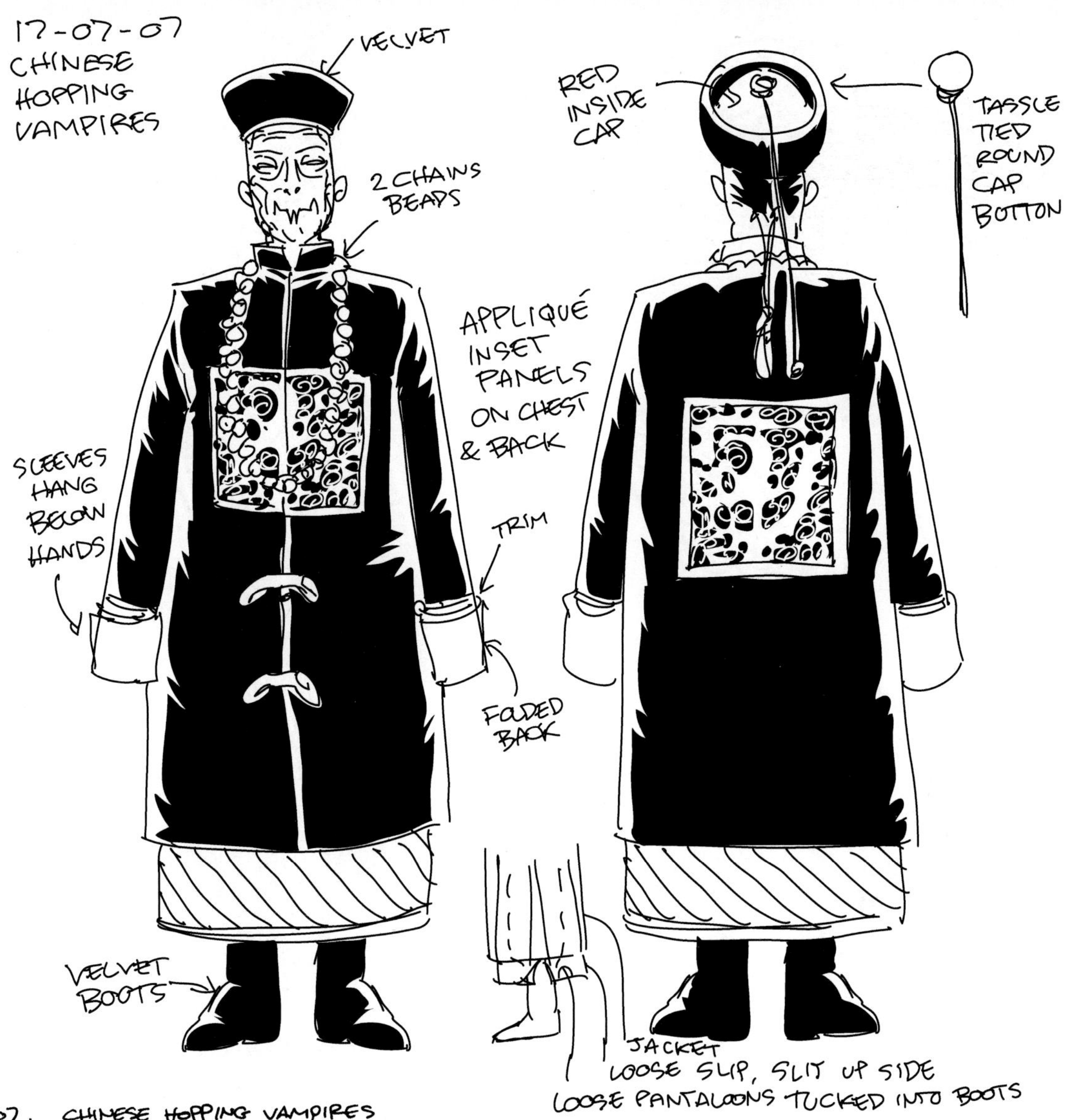

▲ Hopping Vampire costumes, culled from the 1985 Hong Kong action film *Mister Vampire* (*Geungsi Sinsang*).

◄ Defining the different characters of the three vampires.

▲ Gay John was one of the new gang members introduced in England's Glory - I liked the head shot so much, I used it as the basis for his first appearance in episode one.

◀ Gog, Magog and the Druid priest from part one of Mother London.

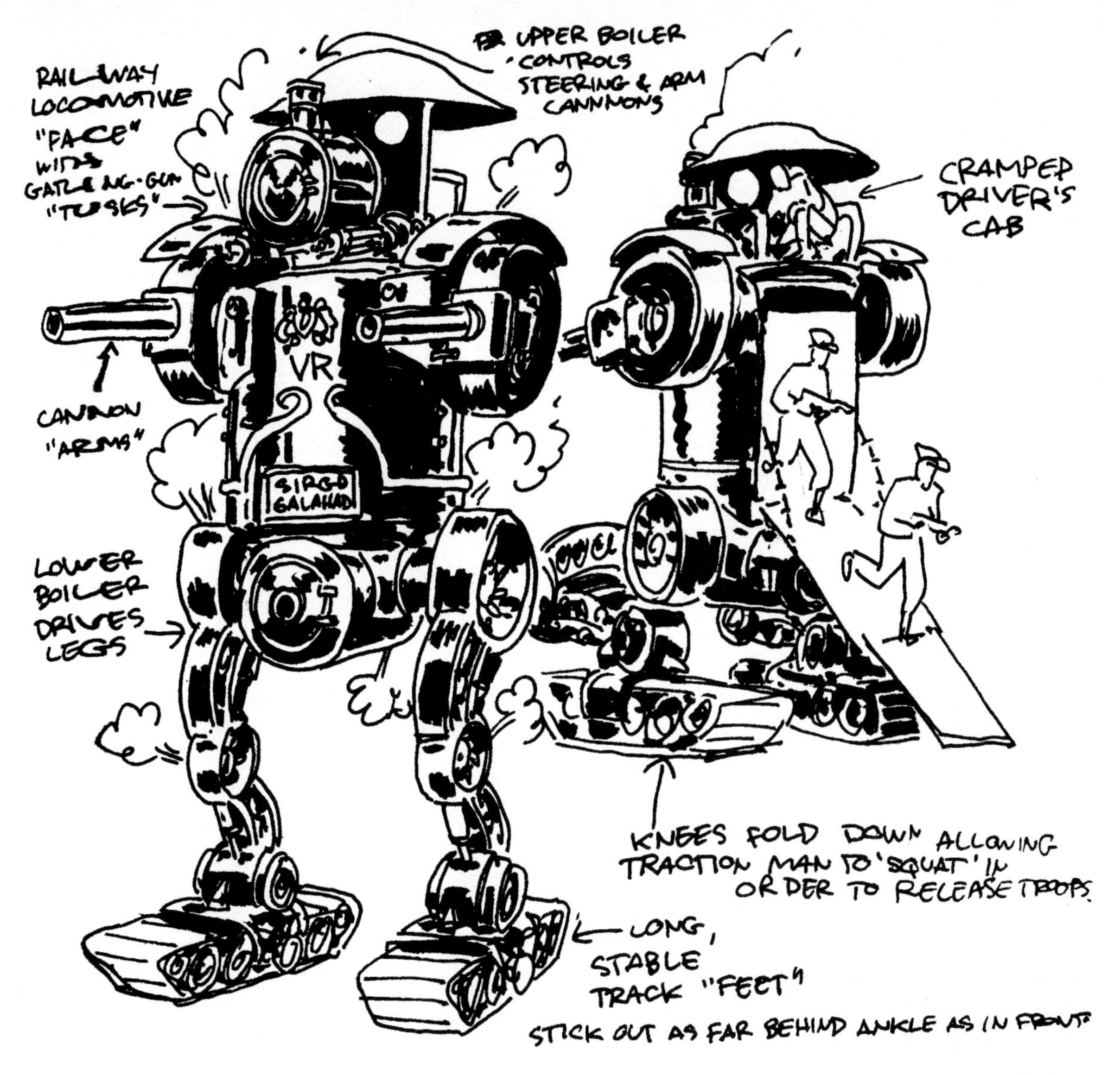

▲ Victorian steam-powered mecha, partly inspired by Ivor the Engine.

► I started Stickleback after moving to a small flat in the centre of Edinburgh. I was surrounded by old stone buildings and cobbled streets, many of which I sampled as textures. This view out of the kitchen window of out flat supplied several textures for the strip.

IAN EDGINTON

Ian Edginton is a relatively recent name to appear in *2000 AD*, but like his *Leviathan* and *Scarlet Traces* co-creator D'Israeli, his impact has been immediate. Already, Edginton is a multiple Eisner award nominee. Debuting with occult pirate series *The Red Seas*, Edginton has gone on to create the aforementioned series as well as *Interceptor, Stickleback, Leviathan* and *Detonator X*. He has also written *Judge Dredd*, a *Kleggs* one-off, and *Strange Cases*.
Edginton's work prior to coming to the Galaxy's Greatest Comic covers a wide range of genres – from Dark Horse's *Aliens* series to *The Authority, Blade, Deadline, The Establishment, Foxfire, Planet of the Apes, Ultraforce* and *Terminator.*

D'ISRAELI

Matt Booker, a.k.a. D'Israeli, is something of a newcomer to *2000 AD* – though his impact, as artist on the creator-owned story *Scarlet Traces*, was immense – leading to some written and drawn *Future Shocks*, and co-creation of the series *XTNCT* and *Leviathan*. However, D'Israeli had already achieved no little fame before coming to the Galaxy's Greatest Comic, working on titles as diverse as *A1, Blast!, Deadline, Kingdom of the Wicked, Lazarus Churchyard* (which was reprinted in the *Megazine*), *Miracleman, Sandman* and *Transmetropolitan*. Brooker was recently the recipient of the Eagle Award for Favourite Comic Artist.